An Introduction to the Structure
of Biological Molecules

PRENTICE-HALL BIOLOGICAL SCIENCE SERIES
William D. McElroy and Carl P. Swanson, *Editors*

PRENTICE-HALL INTERNATIONAL, INC., *London*
PRENTICE-HALL OF AUSTRALIA, PTY. LTD., *Sydney*
PRENTICE-HALL OF CANADA, LTD., *Toronto*
PRENTICE-HALL OF INDIA PRIVATE LTD., *New Delhi*
PRENTICE-HALL OF JAPAN, INC., *Tokyo*

AN INTRODUCTION TO THE STRUCTURE OF BIOLOGICAL MOLECULES

J. M. Barry

University Lecturer
University of Oxford, England

and

E. M. Barry

Prentice-Hall, Inc., Englewood Cliffs, New Jersey

Library of Congress Catalog Card Number 69-17705

Printed in the United States of America

Preface

It has recently become clear that genetics and embryology are founded on the properties of nucleic acid and protein molecules. Moreover, cytology is reaching a stage in which cell structure can be understood in terms of molecular structure. As a result it has become essential for students of biology to extend their knowledge of organic chemistry to include a detailed understanding of the structure of the large molecules on which the structure and function of cells is founded. For this purpose intermediate textbooks of organic chemistry are unsuitable because their emphasis is on organic reactions and the industrial applications of organic chemistry, and because their treatment of natural compounds is inadequate.

In this book we present a discussion of the structures of these biological compounds based on experience of teaching first-year biologists at Oxford. We precede this discussion with two chapters which outline some principles on which the structure of organic molecules is founded. Although this book is intended primarily for biologists it is hoped that the chapters on proteins and nucleic acids will provide students of organic chemistry with information that they cannot conveniently find elsewhere.

J. M. Barry
E. M. Barry

Contents

vii

An Introduction to the Structure
of Biological Molecules

Chapter 1

Some
Structural Principles

1. Bond Angles, Bond Lengths, and Atomic Radii

In the early part of the last century methods were developed for determining the molecular formulae of organic compounds, that is, the number of each kind of atom per molecule. However, these formulae, such as C_2H_6O for ethanol, did little to explain the properties of compounds. Some progress was made when it was found that certain groups of atoms, such as C_6H_5, behave as units, passing unchanged through series of chemical conversions. But a real understanding of the properties of organic compounds only came with the realisation that atoms have definite valencies, and that structural formulae can be written in which atoms are joined by valency bonds. Thus both ethanol and dimethyl ether have the molecular formula C_2H_6O; many of their similarities and differences are explained by their structural formulae:

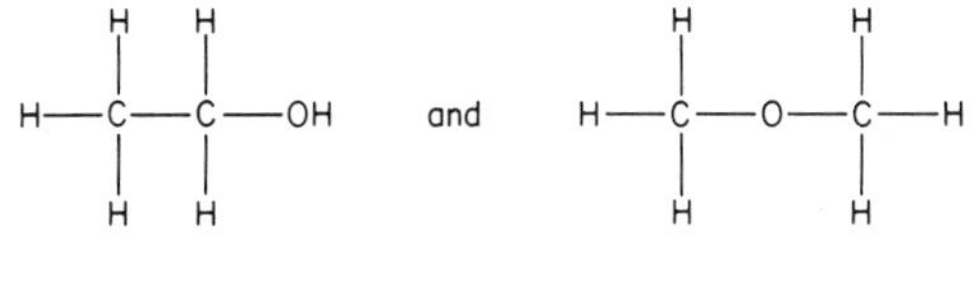

$$
\begin{array}{ccc}
& \text{H} \quad \text{H} & & \text{H} \qquad \text{H} \\
& | \quad\ | & & | \qquad\ | \\
\text{H}-\!&\text{C}-\text{C}-\text{OH} \quad \text{and} \quad \text{H}-&\text{C}-\text{O}-\text{C}-\text{H} \\
& | \quad\ | & & | \qquad\ | \\
& \text{H} \quad \text{H} & & \text{H} \qquad \text{H}
\end{array}
$$

1

A further advance was the understanding of how the valency bonds of carbon are distributed in space. If these four bonds lay in one plane a compound such as methylene dichloride should exist in two isomers:

$$Cl-\underset{\underset{H}{|}}{\overset{\overset{H}{|}}{C}}-Cl \quad \text{and} \quad H-\underset{\underset{Cl}{|}}{\overset{\overset{H}{|}}{C}}-Cl$$

which it does not. It was suggested in 1874 that when carbon is singly bonded to four other groups, its valency bonds are evenly distributed in space. This explains why there is only one methylene dichloride, and why a compound in which four different groups are attached to the same carbon has a mirror-image isomer (see p. 33). Soon after it was suggested that when a double or triple bond is formed between two carbon atoms the valency bonds are distorted from their normal positions; because strain is introduced these bonds are reactive.

More recently the distribution in space of the valency bonds of carbon has been demonstrated by X-ray diffraction. For example, it has been shown that a diamond is composed solely of carbon atoms each of which is covalently linked to four different carbon atoms evenly distributed around it in space:

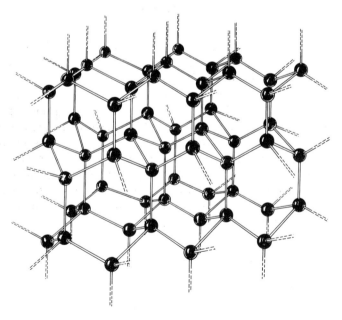

X-ray diffraction measurements on crystals of organic compounds have similarly shown that whenever a carbon atom is linked to four indentical groups these are again evenly distributed in space. This distribution of carbon valency bonds is often called the tetrahedral distribution, because if the ends of four bonds of equal length are joined by straight lines, a regular tetrahedron is formed with the carbon atom in the center. The angles between the valency bonds are 109° 28'. When carbon is linked to four groups that are not identical, these may not be quite evenly distributed in space, but the deviation is seldom large. For example, in methylene difluoride, CH_2F_2, the angle between the two C—F bonds is 108° 17'; in methylene dichloride the angle between the two C—Cl bonds is 111° 47'.

If carbon is linked to another carbon by a double bond, and to two other groups by single bonds, the angle between the single bonds is somewhat larger than 109° as shown by the structure of ethylene:

A single bond attached to a triply bound carbon lies in line with the triple bond, as in acetylene:

X-ray diffraction has also revealed angles between other types of covalent bonds in organic molecules, and these also remain fairly constant. The angle between the C—O—C bonds in ethers such as dimethyl ether is, for example, about 111°.

In addition to bond angles, bond lengths can be determined from X-ray diffraction and other physical measurements. The length of a bond is the distance between the centers of the two bound atoms and, for any two atoms, these do not vary appreciably from compound to compound. For example, the lengths of the single bonds between the carbon atoms of diamond are all 1.54 Å, and all single bonds between carbon atoms in organic compounds are almost exactly this length. (Å is the Ångstrom unit: 10^{-8} cm.) Double bonds between carbon atoms are normally 1.34 Å long, and triple bonds 1.20 Å. [Sometimes carbon atoms which are shown as doubly bonded in normal structural formulae are in fact joined by a bond intermediate in length between a single and double bond, as discussed later (p. 9)]. The bond length between two identical atoms may be halved to give the "bond radius". Thus the single covalent bond radius for carbon is 0.77 Å, while that for oxygen is 0.66 Å. It is found that covalent bond lengths between pairs of different atoms are the sum of the two bond radii; thus a single bond between carbon and oxygen is 1.43 Å long. Some covalent bond radii are shown in Table 1.

Table 1. *Covalent bond radii and van der Waals radii* (Å)

Element	Single bond radius	Double bond radius	van der Waals radius
Carbon	0.77	0.67	—
Hydrogen	0.30	—	1.2
Nitrogen	0.70	0.60	1.5
Oxygen	0.66	0.55	1.4
Sulfur	1.04	0.94	1.9
Phosphorus	1.10	1.00	1.9
Fluorine	0.64	0.54	1.4
Chlorine	0.99	0.89	1.8
Bromine	1.14	1.04	2.0
Iodine	1.33	1.23	2.2

Although atoms are no longer thought of as hard spheres, it is useful to assign them precise radii. Atoms will usually attract one another by van der Waals forces until they reach a distance apart when the force of attraction has fallen to zero. Their distance apart is then said to equal the sum of their atomic radii (or "van der Waals radii"). Atoms do not normally approach one another more closely than their van der Waals radii, since large amounts of energy are needed to make them do so, owing to mutual repulsion. Some of these van der Waals radii are also shown in Table 1. Carbon cannot be given a meaningful atomic radius since its four valency bonds leave none of the surface of the atom exposed for collision. It is seen that atomic radii are larger than bond radii; hence atoms are closer together when bonded than when merely colliding.

Because bond angles, bond radii, and atomic radii in organic compounds are roughly constant, atomic models are manufactured, from which models of molecules can be built which are wholly or partly to scale. Models are of three main kinds. There are first those in which only bond angles are correct; bond lengths are all identical and disproportionately larger than the atomic radii. Such are the familiar models in which different atoms are spheres of different colours, and bonds are springs of uniform length:

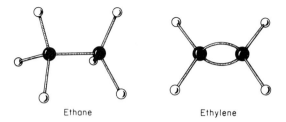

Ethane   Ethylene

These are especially useful for comparing molecules which differ in the distribution of their component groups in space. An atom can be rotated relative to another to which it is joined by a single bond, but this "free rotation" is correctly prevented when two atoms are joined by two or three bent springs representing double or triple bonds.

In the second kind of model, bond angles are correct, but atoms are represented solely by their bonds, which have the correct relative radii:

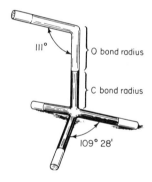

"Framework" model of methanol

Such "framework" models are especially useful for determining distances between atoms in different parts of a molecule, and are convenient because they are not overcrowded with bulky atoms. In the third type of model bond angles are correct, while bond radii and atomic radii are all to scale. In such models the atoms are coloured plastic spheres whose radii are proportional to their atomic radii. Because bond radii are smaller than atomic radii, the spheres are sawn off where rubber pegs representing valency bonds project. These pegs fit into holes in other atoms, and the spheres are pushed as close as they will go to give the correct bond lengths. Shown below are models of a carbon atom with four single bonds, another carbon with two single and one double bond, and a hydrogen atom. Also shown are ethane and ethylene:

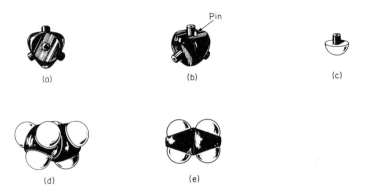

(a)   (b)   (c)

(d)   (e)

Doubly and triply bonded atoms have a metal pin beside the rubber peg to prevent free rotation. These models are particularly useful for discovering whether collision will occur during the rotation of the component groups in a molecule about single bonds, or whether a hypothetical molecule could not exist owing to steric hindrance (i.e., two groups trying to occupy the same space).

2. Uneven Sharing of Electrons in Single Covalent Bonds

A deeper understanding of valency bonds has come from electronic theories of valency. It has become clear that valency bonds in traditional organic structural formulae each represent a pair of electrons shared between the bonded atoms; they are known as covalent bonds. The traditional structural formula of a compound may therefore be called its covalent structure. Although organic chemists are largely concerned with covalent bonding it will be seen later that certain weaker bonds are sometimes involved in stabilising the covalent structure of a molecule in one of its many possible arrangements in space, or "conformations" (see p. 12).

In wave-mechanical theory electrons in atoms are considered to occupy orbitals, which are regions in which the probability of finding an electron is high. The calculations of wave-mechanics show that when a carbon atom forms four single covalent bonds, its four valency electrons occupy four orbitals (known as sp^3) which are inclined to one another at 109° 28'. When two carbon atoms are united by a double bond, electrons in sp^2 orbitals overlap to form one of the bonds. The second bond is formed from two electrons in two $2p$ orbitals and is known as a π bond. It can be proved that this double bonding will prevent rotation of one carbon relative to the other, and that the four remaining valency bonds attached to the two carbons will all lie in one plane.

To a large extent, therefore, modern discoveries have confirmed the conclusions of organic chemists of the last century. However, it has become clear that classical structural formulae misrepresent the structures of compounds in two ways which hinder an understanding of their properties. First, the lines representing valency bonds give no indication that there is, in some of these bonds, a polarisation (separation of positive and negative charge). Such polarisations will be discussed in this section. They can be detected by physical measurements and they influence the properties of compounds in important ways. Second, the clear distinction between double and single bonds is not always correct, as will be discussed in the next section.

When two identical atoms are covalently linked, the pair of electrons of the bond are shared evenly by the two atoms, and there is no separation of charge. However, when the bonded atoms are different, the pair of electrons is always attracted nearer the center of one atom (the more electronegative atom) than the other (the more electropositive). This results in a separation of positive and negative charge: the more electropositive atom can be considered to bear a fraction of a positive charge, and the more electronegative a fraction of a negative charge. An example of this polarisation is in the C—Cl bond. The electrons are attracted closer to the chlorine than the carbon. Classical structural formulae do not indicate polarisation in single covalent bonds. Two ways which have been devised to do this are illustrated for the C—Cl bond:

$$\overset{|}{\underset{|}{-C}} \rightarrow Cl \qquad \text{and} \qquad \overset{|}{\underset{|}{-C}}\overset{\delta+}{}\overset{\delta-}{-Cl}$$

That such polarisations really exist in single covalent bonds is proved by measurements of dipole moments of molecules. These depend on the tendency of polarised molecules to orientate themselves in an electric field, with their positive and negative poles pointing, respectively, towards the negative and positive electrodes. The dipole moment of a molecule is comparable to the magnetic moment of a magnet, and is expressed as the net positive or negative charge within the molecule (in electrostatic units) multiplied by the distance between the positive and negative charges (in units of 10^{-18} cm). The resulting units of dipole moment are named Debye units after P. Debye who developed the concept. The dipole moment of a compound is calculated from its dielectric constant, which depends on the tendency of its molecules to become orientated in an electric field, together with certain other physical constants which compensate for the possibility that the dielectric constant does not result from a permanent polarisation of the molecule, but from one induced by the electric field during measurement.

Methyl chloride has a dipole moment of 1.9D (Debye units) but carbon tetrachloride, in which the C—Cl bonds are evenly distributed in space, has none. Again, nitrobenzene has a dipole moment of 4.2D but *p*-dinitrobenzene, in which the nitro groups are opposed, has none. These, and many similar facts, show that the dipole moment of a molecule is the vector sum of the moments of the individual bonds. From this it is possible to deduce the magnitude and direction of polarisation in various bonds. The dipole moment of nitrobenzene is largely due, not to uneven sharing of electrons, but to the oxygen atoms of the nitro group bearing a fraction of a negative charge for reasons explained later (p. 9). Here, therefore, the direction of polarisation is known:

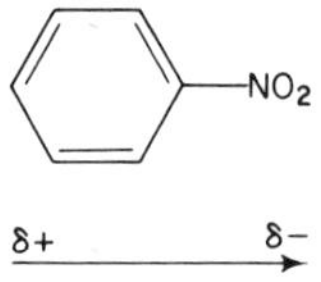

The dipole moment of *p*-chloronitrobenzene is 2.4D. Hence the C—Cl bond must have a moment of about 1.8D in the direction shown:

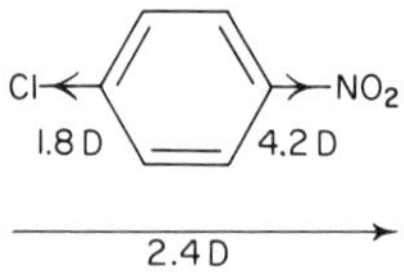

On this principle the dipole moments of many compounds have been analysed into those of the component bonds or, often more conveniently, of the component groups. Some single bond dipole moments due to unequal sharing of electrons between the bonded atoms are:

Bond:	C—Cl	C—Br	C—O	C—N	H—O	H—N
Moment (D):	1.9	1.8	1.2	1.0	1.5	1.3

If a bond which is polarised is attached to a chain of carbon atoms, polarisations will be induced in successive C—C bonds of the chain, the magnitude of each polarisation diminishing with the distance along the chain. This may be illustrated for chlorine attached to a carbon chain as follows:

$$—C \rightarrow C \ggg C \ggg Cl$$

Such induced electron displacements are known as the "inductive effect."

3. Bonds Which Are Intermediate between Double and Single

The clear distinction between double and single bonds in classical structural formulae is not always correct. This may be explained in terms of the concept of resonance, which is one way of expressing certain deductions from wave-mechanics that aid in understanding and predicting the properties of organic compounds. In resonance terminology these deductions are, for convenience, expressed as modifications of classical structural formulae. Students who are not chemistry specialists often find resonance difficult to "understand". This is usually because they are straining after the unattainable. They will never thoroughly understand it unless they understand its basis in quantum mechanics, and this they usually have not time to do. In fact, however, the concept of resonance is designed to offer nonspecialists such as themselves the benefits of wave-mechanics, by giving them rule of thumb methods for predicting certain properties of compounds not suggested by classical structural formulae. These methods are not difficult to understand.

The concept of resonance states that "resonance" will occur in a compound if its molecular structure can be drawn in two or more ways merely by redistributing bonds between atoms, but leaving the positions of the atoms unchanged. The statement "resonance will occur in the compound" is merely meant to imply that the true structure of the compound is intermediate between these different "parent" structures. This true structure is known as the "resonance hybrid", and has certain properties not predictable from the parent structures. Most of the difficulty over resonance has come from the wording. The statement "resonance occurs in the compound" wrongly suggests that some form of vibration is occurring. It is meant to imply that the molecule is permanently in a structure which cannot be expressed by any one conventional structural formula. The more appropriate term *mesomerism*, which implies that the molecule is in a "middle state", has not caught on.

Benzene provides the simplest example of a compound exhibiting

resonance. It can be written in two structures differing only in the
distribution of double and single bonds:

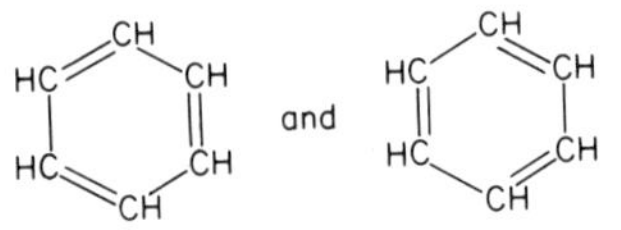

Hence its true structure is intermediate between these parent structures.
The rules of resonance state that the true structure of a compound lies
closest to the parent structure which (if it existed) would have the lowest
energy content. The parent structures for benzene would have identical
energy contents because they contain the same bonds. Hence the true
structure of benzene should lie exactly between these two. That it does so
is supported by measurements of the C—C bond lengths in benzene by
X-ray diffraction. They are all found to be 1.39 Å, intermediate between
the normal 1.34 Å for a double bond and 1.54 Å for a single bond—a
fact which must be remembered when constructing models of carbon
atoms for building benzene rings.

One of the properties that wave-mechanics predicts of a compound
in which resonance occurs is that it will be more stable than expected of
the parent structures. This is so for benzene. For example the heat of
hydrogenation of benzene to cyclohexane is 49.8 kcal/mole:

$$C_6H_6 + 3H_2 \longrightarrow C_6H_{12}$$

The heat of hydrogenation of cyclohexene to cyclohexane is 28.8 kcal/mole:

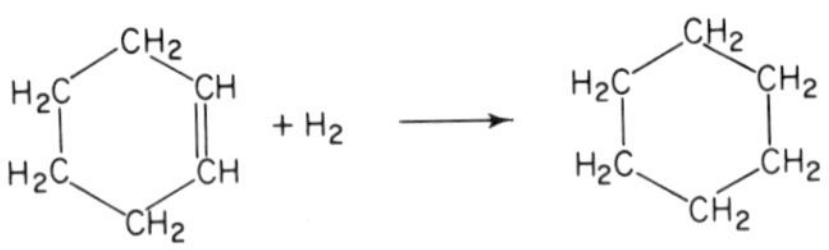

Hence the heat of hydrogenation of either of the parent structures of
benzene would be expected to be about $3 \times 28.8 = 86.4$ kcal/mole. That
the heat of hydrogenation is in fact much lower shows that benzene is in
fact much stabler than expected.

For resonance to occur in a compound its familiar structure must
always contain one or more double bonds, for without them alternative
structures cannot be written. These parent structures may be polarised
(have a separation of positive and negative charge). For example, acetone
can be drawn both in the traditional and in a polarised structure:

$$CH_3-\underset{\underset{O}{\|}}{C}-CH_3 \qquad and \qquad CH_3-\underset{\underset{O^-}{|}}{\overset{+}{C}}-CH_3$$

Hence the true structure of acetone lies between these two, with a lower energy content than predicted for either. But the polarised structure above (if it existed) would be less stable than the familiar structure (if it existed), and hence the true structure of acetone lies closer to the familiar structure. Resonance thus predicts that acetone is polarised, and this is confirmed by its having a dipole moment. The dipole moment of the carbonyl group is 2.3D. Other group dipole moments which result from resonance are that of 3.8D in the nitrile group, and 3.9D in the nitro group which are hybrids between the structures:

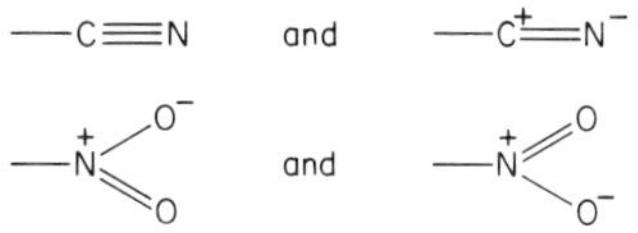

$$-C\equiv N \qquad and \qquad -\overset{+}{C}=N^-$$

$$-\overset{+}{N}\overset{O^-}{\underset{O}{\diagdown}} \qquad and \qquad -\overset{+}{N}\overset{O}{\underset{O^-}{\diagdown}}$$

Although the concept of resonance shows once again that the traditional structural formulae of many compounds are inadequate these are still normally used. Benzene, for example, is still usually shown as one of the two structures with alternating double and single bonds. However, ways of indicating resonance hybrid structures have been devised. One uses curved arrows to indicate how the electron distribution in the true structure differs from that in the conventional structure. Acetone for example may be drawn as:

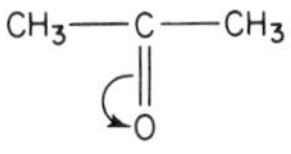

$$CH_3-C-CH_3$$

The tail of the arrow indicates where a pair of electrons should be moved from, and the head where they should be moved to, to give the alternative parent structure. The structure of benzene may similarly be indicated by curved arrows, or by a formula in which all the bonds between carbon atoms are shown to be identical:

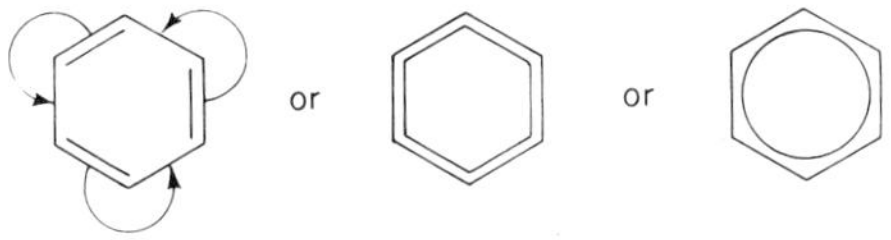

The deductions of wave mechanics that are conveyed in the concept of resonance are sometimes expressed in other terms. For example the electrons whose displacement is indicated by curved arrows in the above formulae are sometimes said to be "delocalised", and this is said to cause the increased stability discussed above.

4. Free Rotation of Groups about Single Bonds

So far in this chapter the covalent bonding of atoms in organic molecules has been considered. But a description of the manner in which the atoms of a molecule are covalently bonded does not usually define its structure in full since alternative arrangements of the atoms in space are usually possible. One way in which different spatial structures can result will be considered in this section: namely by "free" roation of the component groups of a molecule, relative to one another, about single bonds. The different structures formed in this way are known as the different "conformations" of a molecule and are readily interconverted. In the next section, and in the next chapter, "stereoisomers" or different molecules which result from different fixed arrangements in space of identically bonded atoms will be considered. The term *configuration* is used to describe the fixed arrangement in space of the groups of a molecule.

The simplest molecule that can exist in different conformations is ethane, in which two methyl groups are joined by a single bond. By rotating one methyl group relative to the other, two distinct structures can be formed: the "eclipsed", in which the hydrogens of one methyl group eclipse those of the other when the molecule is viewed from one end; and the "staggered", in which the hydrogens of one methyl group lie between those of the other when the molecule is viewed in the same way:

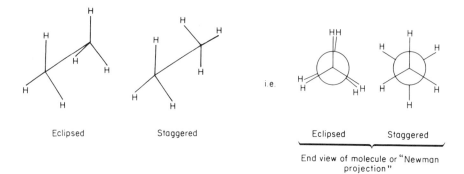

Eclipsed   Staggered   i.e.   Eclipsed   Staggered

End view of molecule or "Newman projection"

(Each structure above is shown in its "sawhorse" formula which gives a three-dimensional view of the molecule, and in its "Newman" formula which shows the relative positions of the groups when viewed from one end of the molecule.)

Between these two conformations are an infinite number of others resulting from infinitely small rotations of one group relative to the other. It was at one time thought that all these conformations of ethane are equally stable, but around 1936 it was proved, by wave-mechanical calculations from certain physical properties of ethane, that this is not so. It was shown that the standard free energy of ethane is about 3 kcal/mole greater in the eclipsed than in the staggered conformation, which is therefore the more stable. In the eclipsed conformation the hydrogens of the two methyl groups are brought closest together, and the lower stability of this conformation results from repulsions between these hydrogens then being maximum. The nature of the repulsive forces is unclear. Molecules of compounds such as these are normally in the stabler staggered conformations. But the energy barrier is not sufficient to prevent them continually passing from one staggered conformation to another, through the eclipsed conformation.

Butane, in which one hydrogen on each methyl group of ethane is replaced by methyl, has two distinct eclipsed conformations. That in which methyl eclipses methyl is less stable than that in which methyl eclipses hydrogen, owing to the repulsion between two methyl groups being greater than between methyl and hydrogen:

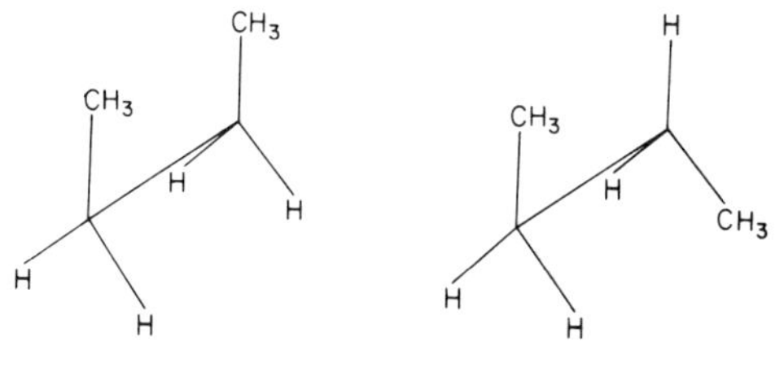

Butane has also two distinct staggered conformations named "anti" and "gauche":

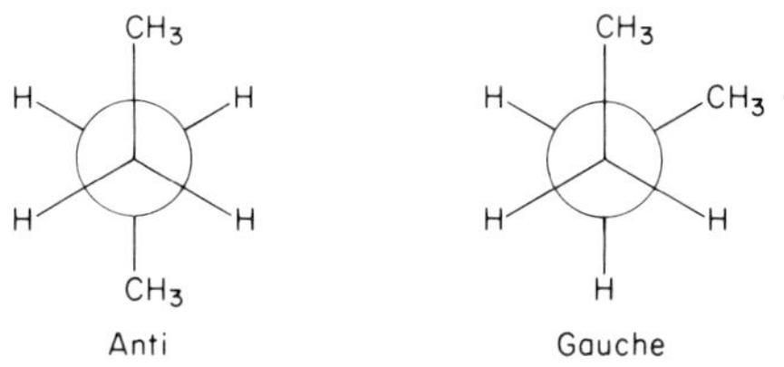

The anti conformation, in which the methyl groups are farthest apart, is the most stable conformation of butane.

For some compounds in which the staggered conformations differ it is possible to determine, by spectral and other measurements, the proportions of the molecules which are in the different conformations. The molecules of solid 1,2-dichloroethane, for example, are all in the anti conformation. The gas is an equilibrium mixture with about two-thirds of the molecules in the anti conformation and one-third in the gauche:

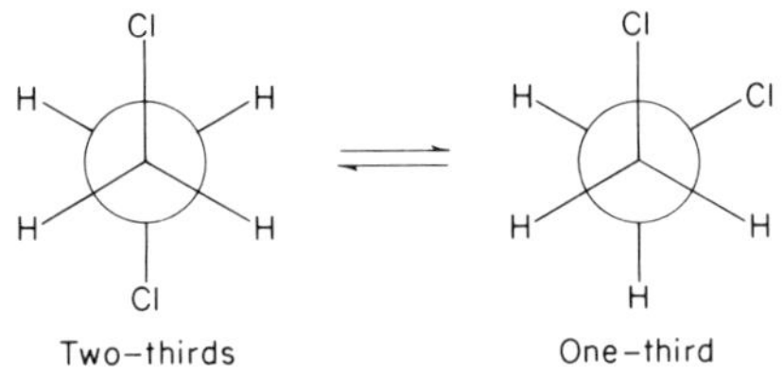

Two-thirds   One-third

Here the anti conformation is stabilised by repulsion between the dipoles in the C—Cl bonds, and in solution the proportion of the anti form varies with the dielectric constant of the solvent. Spectral measurements show that a high proportion of the molecules of ethylene glycol (in carbon tetrachloride solution) exist in the gauche form, in spite of repulsion between the dipoles in the hydroxyls. This is explained by the gauche form being stabilised by hydrogen bonding between the hydroxyls:

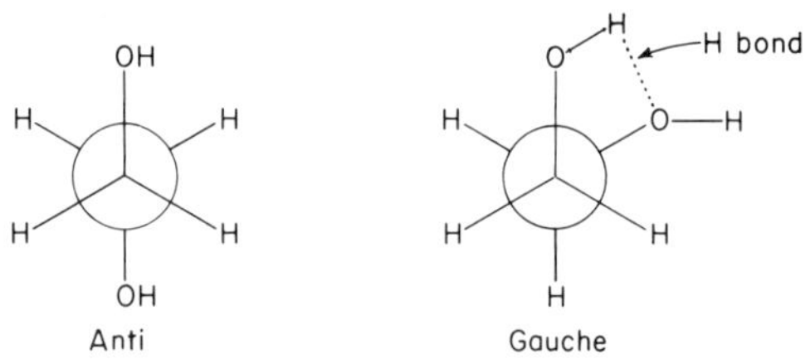

Anti   Gauche

Conformations can also be stabilised by ionic attractions and repulsions, and by van der Waals attractions. Large molecules with many single bonds have enormous numbers of distinct conformations. The biological properties of protein and nucleic acid molecules largely depend on their existing in one particular conformation; if this is destroyed by disrupting the stabilising forces the biological properties of the molecule are lost (see pp. 123 and 158).

Saturated carbon rings can exist in a number of distinct conformations and those of cyclohexane and its derivatives have been very thoroughly investigated. Bond angle strain in rings of six or more carbon atoms is wholly or largely relieved by buckling to give rings which are not flat.

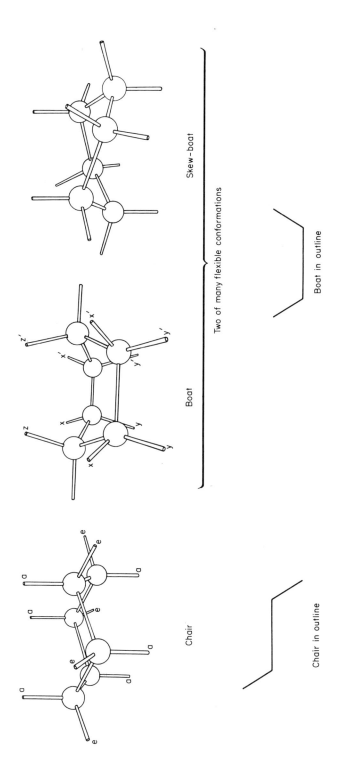

Chair

Boat

Skew-boat

Two of many flexible conformations

Chair in outline

Boat in outline

Models show that cyclohexane can exist in two kinds of nonplanar structure, which are largely free from bond angle strain, known as "chair" and "flexible" conformations: (page 15).

(These structures are conformations because they are interconverted by the partial rotation of the carbon atoms of the ring relative to one another. Complete or "free" rotation of these carbon atoms is, however, prevented by the rigidity of the ring as explained in the next section.) The stabilities of these forms can be predicted by "conformational analysis"—examination of interactions between the component groups. The following considerations show that the chair conformation is the stablest. The C—H bonds in the chair form above have been lettered a for "axial" or e for "equatorial". The axial bonds are perpendicular to the ring, while the equatorial bonds are roughly in line with it. It can be seen that if a carbon atom has its axial bond pointing above the ring, the carbon atoms on either side of it each have their axial bonds pointing below the ring. Hence all C—H bonds are staggered relative to those on adjacent carbon atoms.

In the boat conformation, on the other hand, the C—H bonds lettered x and x' eclipse one another when viewed from the end of the molecule, as do those lettered y and y'. Eclipsed conformations are less stable than staggered. Also, the hydrogens lettered z and z' are closer than the sum of their van der Waals radii and hence, in fact, must repel one another and introduce strain into the molecule. It can be deduced that other flexible conformations will be stabler than the boat but less stable than the chair. These conclusions are confirmed by physical measurements which show that cyclohexane molecules are virtually entirely in the chair conformation.

In the chair conformation each carbon has one axial and one equatorial C—H bond. Manipulation of models shows that the chair conformation can be converted, by partial rotation of carbon atoms about single bonds, into another chair conformation. This is identical to the first except that those C—H bonds that were equatorial are now axial, and *vice versa*. This conversion involves passing through a flexible conformation which presents an energy barrier, but physical measurements show that cyclohexane molecules, at normal temperatures, do continually undergo the conversion:

In cyclohexane the two chair conformations are equally stable, but in cyclohexane derivatives this is usually not so. For example, models suggest that in methyl cyclohexane the chair conformation with equatorial methyl is the more stable. This is because the C—methyl bond is then anti (see p. 13) to the C—C bonds on adjacent carbons, rather than gauche as it is when the methyl group is axial. This prediction is confirmed by evidence that methyl cyclohexane is an equilibrium mixture with about 95% of the molecules in a chair conformation with equatorial methyl and 5% in a chair conformation with axial methyl:

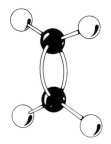

95%   5%

Many sugars have six-membered rings which exist in chair conformations similar to those of cyclohexane derivatives. Conformational analysis can predict, as with methylcyclohexane, whether groups will tend to be attached to these rings by axial or equatorial bonds. This facilitates an understanding of the properties of sugars (see p. 68).

5. Restricted Rotation of Groups

In the last section the different structures which molecules can assume as a result of the rotation of their component groups about single bonds were considered. These structures are readily interconverted. If this "free rotation" between adjacent atoms is restricted, then different structures which are not readily interconverted can result. Such stereoisomers are known as "geometrical isomers" and will be discussed in this section.

The simplest examples of geometrical isomerism are provided by compounds in which free rotation between adjacent carbon atoms is prevented by a double bond, as in derivatives of ethylene. In ethylene the four C—H bonds all lie in one plane:

Hence, when one hydrogen of each methylene group is replaced by a substituent X two stereoisomers are possible: one in which the X groups are adjacent (known as the *cis* isomer) and one in which they are opposed (known as the *trans*):

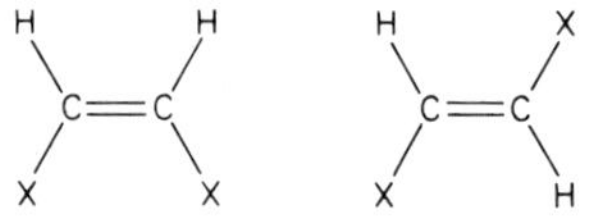

cis   trans

Examples of such isomers are maleic and fumaric acids:

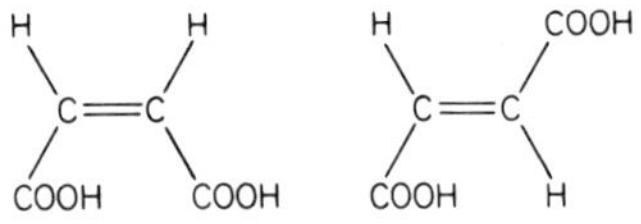

Maleic acid   Fumaric acid

Like most geometrical isomers they have very different properties owing to the different distances between the component groups. Thus the melting points of fumaric and maleic acids are $287°$ and $130°$ respectively. Their solubilities in water at $25°$ are 0.7 and 79 gm/100 ml respectively. Because the carboxyl groups of maleic acid are adjacent it yields an anhydride on gentle heating:

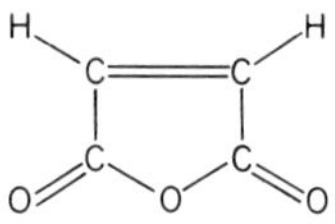

Maleic anhydride

Fumaric acid does not form a similar anhydride, but on strong heating the molecule rearranges to give maleic anhydride. Other examples of *cis-trans* isomers are oleic and elaidic acids, found in fats:

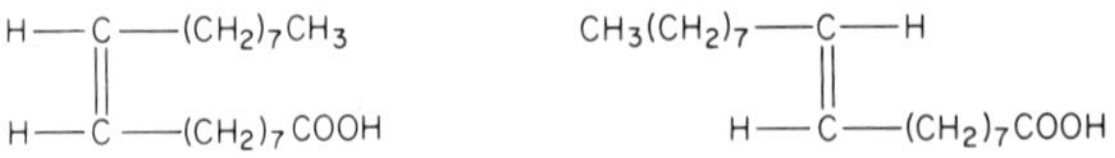

Oleic acid   Elaidic acid

Geometrical isomerism also occurs in saturated ring compounds, for although the carbon atoms of the ring are joined by single bonds, their complete rotation relative to one another is prevented by the rigidity of the ring. The simplest examples are in derivatives of cyclopropane in which the ring is flat. Thus, cyclopropane-1,2-dicarboxylic acid exists in *cis* and *trans* isomers in which the carboxyl groups are respectively on the same side, and on opposite sides, of the plane of the ring:

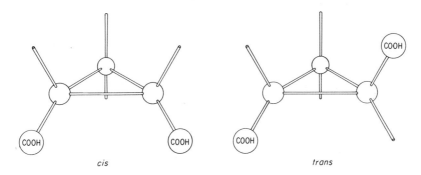

cis   *trans*

Larger cycloparaffin rings are not flat and, because changes in conformation can occur as a result of partial rotation between carbon atoms, the relative positions of the groups in *cis* and *trans* isomers is more complicated. 1,2-Dimethylcyclohexane provides a relatively simple illustration. It has been seen that cyclohexane normally exists in a "chair" conformation, each carbon having one axial and one equatorial C—H bond (see p. 16). The *trans* isomer of 1,2-dimethylcyclohexane can therefore exist in diaxial and diequatorial forms. Conformational analysis shows that almost all the molecules must be diequatorial (although the two C—CH₃ bonds are gauche, they are both anti to C—C ring bonds on adjacent carbons):

$$H_3C\!-\!\!\quad\quad\quad H_3C\!-\!$$

The *cis* isomer can only exist with one substituent axial and the other equatorial:

$$CH_3 \quad\quad H_3C\!-\!$$

But such molecules continually undergo a change in conformation, the bonds which were axial becoming equatorial and *vice versa* (see p. 16).

Although such rings are not flat, it is simplest when it is merely desired to illustrate whether groups are *cis* or *trans* to draw the rings flat, with *trans* substituents projecting in opposite directions. Thus *cis* and *trans* 1,2-dimethylcyclohexanes are conveniently represented:

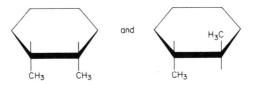

Sugar rings are also usually drawn flat to emphasise in the simplest possible way whether hydroxyl groups are *cis* or *trans* (see p. 67).

When two saturated carbon rings are fused by having two carbons in common, *cis* and *trans* isomerism occurs at the junction of the two rings, a fact which is important in steroid chemistry. The simplest examples of this type of isomerism are provided by *cis*- and *trans*- decalin in which two cyclohexane rings are fused:

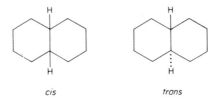

In *cis*-decalin the two hydrogens at the junction between the rings are on the same side of the two rings, and in *trans*-decalin they are on opposite sides. This difference is represented in the following formulae in which the two rings are understood to be in the plane of the paper, while the C—H bonds at the junction of the rings are directed below the paper if shown dotted, and above it if shown solid:

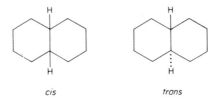

This is the convention used in representing configurations at the junctions of steroid rings. But in fact the rings are not planar: in both isomers the rings are in the chair conformation:

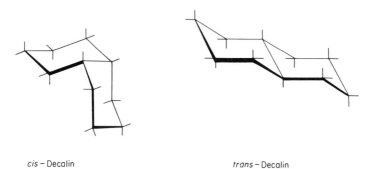

cis – Decalin   *trans* – Decalin

It is seen that in *trans*-decalin both hydrogens at the ring junction are axial in relation to both rings. In *cis*-decalin the two hydrogens are axial and equatorial, respectively, in relation to one ring, and equatorial and axial, respectively, in relation to the other ring. *Cis*-Decalin can readily change its conformation into another that is identical except that every bond that was axial becomes equatorial, and *vice versa*. The heat of combustion of *cis*-decalin is greater than that of *trans*-decalin. This fact can readily be explained by conformational analysis which shows that steric interactions are greater in *cis*- than in *trans*-decalin.

When one hydrogen on each of the carbons of cyclohexane is replaced by the same group, eight geometrical isomers are possible. Such are the inositols, many of which occur in living organisms:

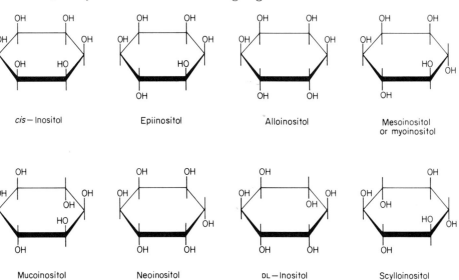

cis – Inositol   Epiinositol   Alloinositol   Mesoinositol or myoinositol

Mucoinositol   Neoinositol   DL – Inositol   Scylloinositol

6. Determination of the Structures of Organic Molecules by Physical Methods

The traditional method of deducing the covalent structure of an organic compound is to apply chemical tests for its component groups, and also to identify compounds which are formed by its degradation. The proposed structure is then confirmed by synthesis. This approach is still used, but in recent years it has increasingly been supplemented by physical methods which give information about the covalent bonding and about the conformation of molecules. The most important of these methods are summarised below.

A. Nuclear magnetic resonance spectroscopy (NMR) and electron spin resonance spectroscopy (ESR)

Nuclear magnetic resonance is based on the fact that compounds can absorb radiation of radio frequencies as a consequence of the magnetic moments of their atomic nuclei. The compound (1–10 mg) is dissolved in a solvent which does not give interfering absorption such as carbon tetrachloride, and is put in the sample chamber of the NMR spectrometer, a machine which is produced commercially. The sample lies in an electromagnetic field and is exposed to radiofrequency oscillations of a fixed frequency. The strength of the magnetic field is gradually varied, and at certain field strengths the compound will absorb the radiofrequency energy. When it does, the intensity of absorption is recorded by a radiofrequency detector. The NMR spectrogram, which the instrument automatically delivers after a few minutes, is a plot of the intensity of absorption against the magnetic field strength.

Atoms with even numbers of protons and even numbers of neutrons do not contribute to the absorption. Hence the normal isotopes of carbon ($^{12}_{6}C$) and of oxygen ($^{16}_{8}O$) do not absorb, and therefore the absorption of an organic compound is largely due to its hydrogen atoms. The magnetic field strength at which these absorb depends on their position in the molecule. A compound with all hydrogens identically placed, such as methyl chloride, gives only one main absorption peak. A compound with hydrogens in two types of position, such as ethyl chloride, gives two main peaks; and so on. Moreover, the areas under the peaks are proportional to the number of hydrogen atoms responsible for the absorption. With ethyl chloride, for example, these areas are in the ratio 3:2.

Hence the number of main peaks, and their areas, can give important information about a compound. Also, conclusions about the particular groups in which hydrogen atoms occur can be drawn from the field strengths of the absorption peaks. Moreover if the spectrum is plotted at greater resolution, by having smaller increments of field strength between measurements, the main peaks often show subdivisions. The number of these is related to the number of hydrogen atoms on carbons adjacent to that which bears the hydrogen responsible for the main peak. In simple molecules, the number of subdivisions is one greater than the number of adjacent hydrogens.

It is often possible to deduce the complete structure of simple compounds from their NMR spectra. For example, suppose we are given two compounds of molecular formula C_2H_6O. One gives only one peak showing that all its hydrogens are similarly placed. Hence its structure must be $CH_3 \cdot O \cdot CH_3$. The other gives three main peaks of relative areas

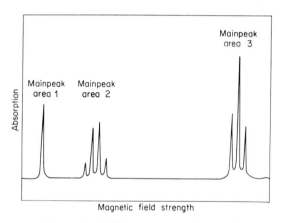

Figure 1. NMR spectrum of ethanol

3:2:1. Hence it has a multiple of three hydrogens of one type, two of another and one of another. Greater resolution gives the spectrum of Figure 1. The peak of area 3 now has three subdivisions showing that there are two hydrogens on adjacent carbons. The peak of area 2 has four subdivisions showing that there are three hydrogens on adjacent carbons. Hence the structure of the compound is $CH_3 \cdot CH_2 \cdot OH$. NMR can be applied even to complex compounds such as steroids, and can give important information about their component groups and their conformations.

Electron spin resonance spectroscopy is somewhat similar to NMR spectroscopy. Absorption is due to unpaired electrons and is therefore given by free radicals. From the absorption bands, information can be deduced about the structures of the free radicals which are formed from a compound, and hence about the structure of the compound itself.

B. Infrared, ultraviolet, and visible spectroscopy

All organic compounds absorb infrared light, and with an infrared spectrophotometer a spectrum can be determined in a few minutes on less than one milligramme of a compound. The spectrum is a plot of the intensity of absorption against wave length. It appears as a profile of jagged peaks of varying height which is characteristic of the compound, and hence can be used as a "fingerprint" for its identification. If a known and unknown compound give infrared spectra which are superimposable it can almost certainly be concluded that they are identical. Many functional groups, such as hydroxyl and carbonyl, give absorption bands at a roughly constant wavelength irrespective of the compound in which they occur, and hence can be identified. Moreover, slight but characteristic variations in the positions of these absorption bands are caused by certain neighbouring groups which can be identified in this way. As a result, a large amount of information about the structures of compounds can, with experience, be deduced from their infrared spectra.

Many compounds also absorb ultraviolet light (wave lengths below 400 mμ), and colored compounds absorb visible light (wave lengths between about 400 and 800 mμ). Spectrometers can be bought which will automatically plot ultraviolet and visible spectra of compounds. These have fewer absorption bands than infrared spectra but conclusions can sometimes again be drawn from them about the structure of a compound. For example compounds with isolated double bonds absorb in the ultraviolet around 165 mμ. Compounds with conjugated double bonds absorb more intensely at longer wave lengths, the intensity and wave length increasing with the extent of conjugation.

C. Mass spectrometry

A mass spectrometer has three main sections: an ionisation chamber in which the compound under examination is converted into positive ions by bombardment with electrons; an analyser in which the ions are separated according to their ratio of mass to charge; and a dectector which determines the quantity of each ion. Most of the ions have a charge of one, and hence they are separated according to their mass. One of the ions is always formed by the loss of one electron from the parent compound, while the remainder are ionised fragments formed by its degradation. One application of mass spectrometry is that the molecular weight of the parent ion can be determined with an accuracy of at least 0.1%. This is particularly useful for compounds of intermediate molecular weights (of around 1000) which cannot be accurately determined in other ways.

If the mass of an ion is determined with great accuracy it is often possible to deduce its molecular formula. For example it could be concluded that an ion of molecular weight 58.078 is $C_4H_{10}^+$ rather than $C_3H_6O^+$ (molecular weight 58.042). Molecular formulae can also be deduced in another way. In addition to the main peak due to an ion there will be another smaller one which has a molecular weight one unit greater. This is because occasional ions will have a carbon atom which is the stable isotope ^{13}C rather than the normal ^{12}C; others will have a hydrogen atom which is ^2H or an oxygen atom which is ^{17}O, or a nitrogen atom which is ^{15}N. These occur with differing abundance. Thus ^{13}C forms 1.11% of ^{12}C, ^2H forms 0.015% of ^1H, ^{17}O forms 0.04% of ^{16}O, and ^{15}N forms 0.37% of ^{14}N. As a result, the height of the peak of +1 molecular weight will depend on the numbers of each kind of atom in the ion. For example the ion $C_3H_6NO^+$ will have a main peak at mass 72; its peak at 73 will be $3 \times 1.11 + 6 \times 0.015 + 0.37 + 0.04 = 3.83\%$ of the height of the main peak. The ion $C_2H_2NO_2^+$ will also have a main peak at 72; but its peak at 73 will be $2 \times 1.11 + 2 \times 0.015 + 0.37 + 2 \times 0.04 = 2.70\%$ of the height of the main peak. Compounds with oxygen and chlorine atoms also have peaks at +2 molecular weight due to ^{18}O and ^{37}Cl. Tables have been prepared giving the ratios of peak sizes to be expected for different molecular formulae. These methods enable the molecular formulae of a parent ion and the ions formed by its degradation to be determined, and from this information many facts can often be deduced about the structure of the original compound. Moreover, compounds with certain groups often give characteristic fragments: for example, a compound with a hydroxyl group will usually lose water to give an ion which is 18 molecular weight units lighter than itself.

D. Optical rotatory dispersion

Dissymmetric compounds rotate the plane of polarised light (see p. 35) and this optical rotation varies with the wave length of the light. The technique of optical rotatory dispersion is to plot the optical rotation of a dissymmetric compound against the wave length of the polarised light, from the visible region down to the practical limit of wave lengths of about 250 mμ in the ultraviolet. Curves of two kinds are obtained as shown in Figure 2. If the compound absorbs light of the wave lengths used the optical rotation rises to a peak as the wave length decreases, and then rapidly falls through zero rotation to a maximum rotation in the opposite direction. This reversal of the direction of optical rotation is known as the "Cotton effect" and occurs near the wave length at which the absorption of ultraviolet light by the compound is maximum. This type of curve, and the more complex one which results when the compound absorbs at two or more wave lengths, are called "anomalous" (shown solid). If the compound does not absorb at the wave length used, a "plain curve" is obtained (shown dotted). Since all compounds absorb in the far ultraviolet the plain curve merely appears to be the ascending part of an anomalous curve before the peak is reached.

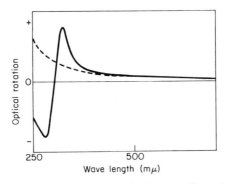

Figure 2. Anomalous and plain optical rotary dispersion curves.

Optical rotatory dispersion measurements are most useful on compounds with which a Cotton effect can be demonstrated. It is often possible to draw conclusions about their structures from the sizes of the peaks and troughs, and the wave lengths at which they occur. The following are a few examples from many possible ones. Steroids with a keto group in position 1 (see p. 176) give different curves from those with a keto group in position 2 or 3. The ring size of a cyclic ketone can often be deduced by comparison of its curves with those of ketones of known ring size. The conformation of a ring compound can often be deduced by comparison of its curves with those of compounds of known conformation. Less can be concluded about compounds that give plain curves, but there is an important application to proteins: α-helical peptides (see p. 116) give different plain curves to those in random coils, and this enables the proportion of the amino acids of a protein that are in α-helices to be deduced.

E. X-ray diffraction

When X-rays are passed in the correct manner through a crystal of a compound a diffraction pattern results owing to regular variations in electron density within the crystal. If the X-rays are allowed to fall on a photographic plate the diffraction pattern shows up as a pattern of spots of varying intensity. From these intensities, and the distances between the spots, it is often possible to deduce the distances between the atoms in the molecules of the crystal, since the atoms are the centres of high electron density. An X-ray diffraction study of a single compound requires a long series of measurements and calculations, which are impossible to explain briefly.

Studies of crystals of simple compounds of known structural formulae have given information about the lengths of the various bonds found in organic compounds and the angles between them. X-ray diffraction has also been used to deduce the structural formulae of some compounds, the most important being vitamin B_{12}. A most important application of the method in biology is to deduce the conformation of organic molecules in crystals—not only of small molecules such as sugars, but also of nucleic acid and protein molecules (see pp. 115 and 154). Also, when molecules are arranged regularly in a biological structure this arrangement can sometimes be deduced. For example, tobacco mosaic virus particles have been shown by X-ray diffraction to have a single helical molecule of RNA surrounded by a helical arrangement of many protein molecules.

7. Naming of Organic Molecules to Indicate Their Structures

In the early days of organic chemistry there were no systematic rules for naming organic compounds, and a name was usually assigned to a compound according to the fancy of its discoverer. These names often referred to the source of the compound and such names are still convenient for familiar compounds, such as uric acid rather than 2,6,8-trihydroxypurine, and they are still assigned and used (e.g., penicillin from the mold *Penicillium*). But for the thousands of less familiar organic compounds it is more efficient to use names that give at least some indication of their structure.

The systematic naming of organic compounds is organised by a committee of the International Union of Pure and Applied Chemistry. A compound is most often named as if it were a derivative of a familiar parent compound. A very simple example is aminoacetic acid for the amino acid glycine; that is, the amino derivative of the familiar parent compound acetic acid. Rules have been laid down as to how names of this kind should be devised, and the more important are summarised below.

Saturated aliphatic hydrocarbons are named as if they were derivatives of a hydrocarbon with the longest unbranched chain in the molecule. The names of the groups attached to this hydrocarbon are placed in alphabetical order before its name, and a number is placed before each group to show its point of attachment. These numbers refer to successive carbons in the straight chain, the numbering being started from the end of the chain that will give the first substituent along it the smallest number. Thus, the following is not named 2- or 5-ethylhexane, or 2- or 3-butylbutane, or 5-methylheptane, but 3-methylheptane:

$$
\begin{array}{cccccccc}
 & & & & \overset{\displaystyle CH_3}{|} & & \\
CH_3 & \!\!-\!\!CH_2 & \!\!-\!\!CH_2 & \!\!-\!\!CH_2 & \!\!-\!\!CH & \!\!-\!\!CH_2 & \!\!-\!\!CH_3 \\
7 & 6 & 5 & 4 & 3 & 2 & 1
\end{array}
$$

Another example is 3-ethyl-2-methylhexane:

$$
\begin{array}{ccccc}
 & & & \overset{\displaystyle C_2H_5}{|} & \overset{\displaystyle CH_3}{|} \\
CH_3 & \!\!-\!\!CH_2 & \!\!-\!\!CH_2 & \!\!-\!\!CH & \!\!-\!\!CH & \!\!-\!\!CH_3
\end{array}
$$

Aliphatic hydrocarbons with one double bond are named as if they were derivatives of the hydrocarbon with the longest unbranched chain in the molecule which contains the double bond. This hydrocarbon is named by changing the ending -*ane* of the corresponding saturated hydro-carbon to -*ene*. Its chain is numbered from the end that will give the carbon atoms of the double bond the smallest possible numbers; and the position of the double bond is indicated by placing the number of the first of its two carbons before the name of the hydrocarbon. The points of attachment of other substituents are indicated as before. Similar principles are applied to hydrocarbons with more than one double bond. These principles are illustrated by the following:

$$
\begin{array}{ccccc}
 & & \overset{\displaystyle CH_3}{|} & \overset{\displaystyle C_2H_5}{|} & \\
CH_3 & \!\!-\!\!CH_2 & \!\!-\!\!CH & \!\!-\!\!C & \!\!=\!\!CH_2
\end{array}
$$
2-Ethyl-3-methyl-1-pentene

$$
\begin{array}{cccccc}
 & \overset{\displaystyle CH_3}{|} & & & \overset{\displaystyle CH_3}{|} & \\
CH_2 & \!\!=\!\!C & \!\!-\!\!CH_2 & \!\!-\!\!CH_2 & \!\!-\!\!C & \!\!=\!\!CH_2
\end{array}
$$
2,5-Dimethyl-1,5-hexadiene

Cyclic hydrocarbons are named as if they were derivatives of a familiar cyclic hydrocarbon, the numbering of whose carbons has been specified. The basic heterocyclic compounds have similarly been numbered by con-vention. The smallest possible numbers are chosen for substituent groups.

Carbons 1 and 2 of napthalene are also known as α and β. In disubstituted benzenes positions 2, 3, and 4 are also known as *ortho*, *meta*, and *para*. Examples are:

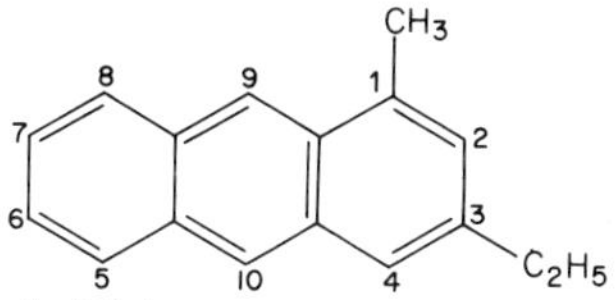

3-Ethyl-1-methylanthracene

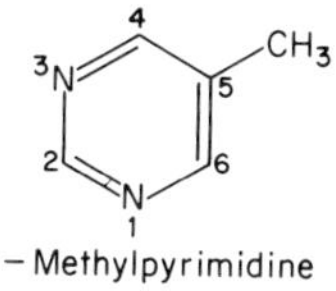

5-Methylpyrimidine

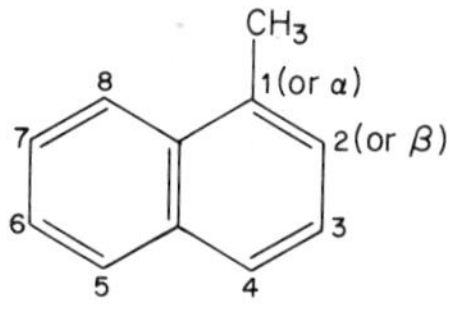

1-Methylnaphthalene
or α-Methylnaphthalene

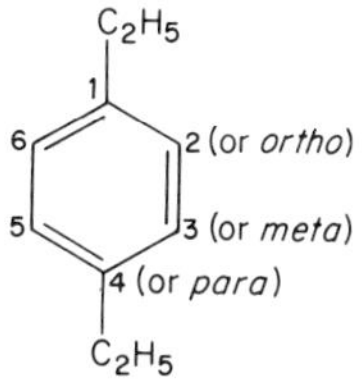

p-Diethylbenzene
or 1,4-Diethylbenzene

Compounds that contain functional groups are sometimes named as derivatives of hydrocarbons. The functional groups are then normally listed alphabetically before the name of the hydrocarbon using conventional abbreviations. These include alkoxy- for ether groups; amino-; carboxamido- for amide; carboxy-; chloro- etc. for halogens; cyano-; hydroxy-; mercapto-; nitro-.

Alternatively, compounds with a number of functional groups are named as derivatives of a compound with one of these functional groups. This one group is selected on a conventional order of preference which includes the following groups in the order shown; $COOH > SO_3H$ or $SO_2NH_2 > CONH_2$ or CN or $COOR > CHO > NH_2 > OH$. Thus glycine is named aminoacetic acid and not carboxymethylamine. In derivatives of open-chain compounds the carbons of the chain are numbered from the carbon of the principal functional group (or the adjacent carbon if it has no carbon). Alternatively the carbons of the chain are given Greek letters starting with the carbon adjacent to the functional group as α; the letter ω always designates the last carbon in a chain whatever its length. The parent compound with the principal functional group is given a name with an ending that denotes this group. The endings used include: -oic acid or -carboxylic acid; -sulphonic acid; -sulphonamide; -amide or -carboxamide; -nitrile; -al for aldehyde; -amine; and -ol for alcoholic hydroxyl. These principles are illustrated in the following examples:

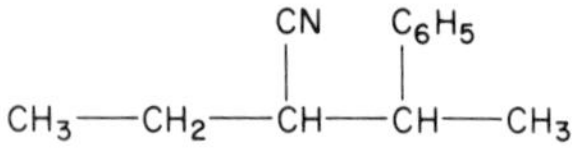

$$\underset{\text{2-Phenyl-3-cyanopentane}}{CH_3—CH_2—\underset{\underset{CN}{|}}{CH}—\underset{\underset{C_6H_5}{|}}{CH}—CH_3}$$

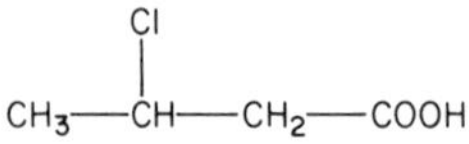

$$\underset{\text{3- or } \beta\text{-Chlorobutyric acid}}{CH_3—\underset{\underset{Cl}{|}}{CH}—CH_2—COOH}$$

$$\underset{\text{4- or } \omega\text{-Hydroxybutylamine (not 4- or } \omega\text{-aminobutanol)}}{HO—CH_2—CH_2—CH_2—CH_2—NH_2}$$

$$\underset{\text{4- or } \omega\text{-Chlorobutanol (not 4- or } \omega\text{-hydroxybutylchloride)}}{Cl—CH_2—CH_2—CH_2—CH_2—OH}$$

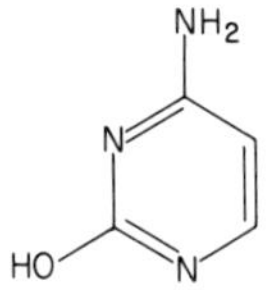

4–Amino–2–hydroxypyrimidine
(Note alphabetical order of substituents)

Some other terms found in chemical names are: the prefix *n-* specifies the isomer that has an unbranched chain; *iso-* indicates that the compound is an isomer of another familiar compound, e.g., isoleucine; *cyclo-* indicates the presence of a ring, e.g., cyclohexane; *spiro* indicates that there are two rings with a single carbon in common; *sym-* and *unsym-* distinguishes between symmetrical and unsymmetrical isomers; *sec-* and *tert-* indicate secondary and tertiary radicals, i.e., branched aliphatic radicals in which the carbon linked to the functional group bears one hydrogen and no hydrogens respectively. Some of the more common radicals are shown below:

$$\underset{\text{Vinyl}}{CH_2{=\!=}CH—}$$ $$\underset{\text{Allyl}}{CH_2{=\!=}CH—CH_2—}$$ Phenyl

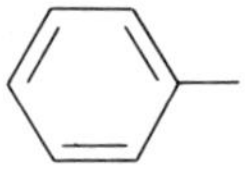

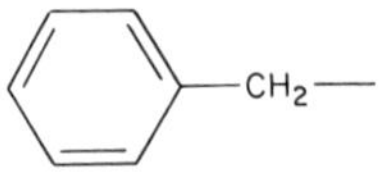

Benzyl   α–Naphthyl   β–Naphthyl

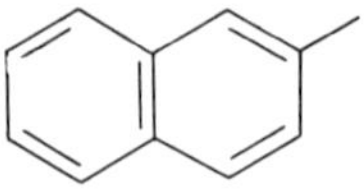

$$\underset{n\text{–Butyl}}{CH_3—CH_2—CH_2—CH_2—}$$ $$\underset{sec\text{–Butyl}}{CH_3—CH_2—\underset{\underset{CH_3}{|}}{CH}—}$$ $$\underset{tert\text{–Butyl}}{CH_3—\underset{\underset{CH_3}{\overset{\overset{CH_3}{|}}{|}}}{C}—}$$ $$\underset{\text{Isobutyl}}{CH_3—\underset{\underset{CH_3}{|}}{CH}—CH_2—}$$

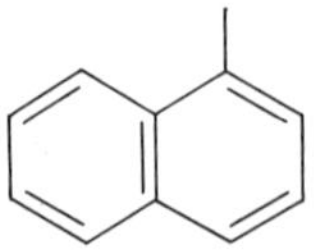

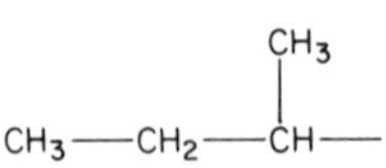

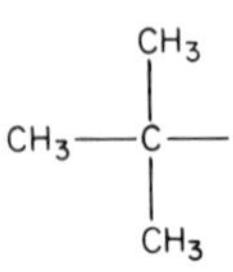

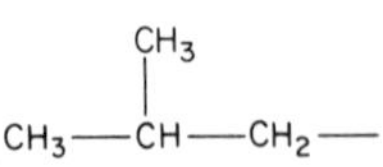

FURTHER READING

1. T. A. Geissman, *Principles of Organic Chemistry*, Freeman & Co., San Francisco, 1962. A textbook with the basic principles of organic structure very well discussed.

2. E. L. Eliel, *Stereochemistry of Carbon Compounds*, McGraw-Hill, New York, 1962.

3. J. D. Roberts, *Nuclear Magnetic Resonance*, McGraw-Hill, New York, 1959. Clear explanation of the basis of the method and of its application to organic chemistry.

4. J. C. D. Brand and G. Eglinton, *Applications of Spectroscopy to Organic Chemistry*, Oldbourne Press, London, 1965. Describes principles and practice of nuclear magnetic resonance, infrared and ultraviolet spectroscopy.

5. F. H. C. Crick and J. C. Kendrew, *X-ray Analysis and Protein Structure*, Advances in Protein Chemistry, **12** (1957), 133. Clear explanation of the principles of X-ray diffraction.

6. G. J. Bullen, *X-ray Diffraction*, Comprehensive Biochemistry 3 (1962) 33, Elsevier Publishing Co., Amsterdam.

Chapter 2

Molecular Dissymmetry

1. Molecules With One Asymmetric Carbon Atom

This chapter will be devoted to a discussion of fixed arrangements of atoms in space which result in "dissymmetric" molecules. (The word *dissymmetric* is used to denote a structure that cannot be superimposed on its mirror image, such as a right-handed glove which cannot be super-imposed on a left-handed glove. Some such structures have certain elements of symmetry and hence the more familiar term *asymmetric*—without symmetry—cannot strictly be used.) Since atoms are themselves symmetrical it follows that the atoms in a dissymmetric molecule can always be arranged in an alternative way to give a molecule which is the mirror image of the first. A pair of isomers that are mirror images are known as "enantiomers", and stereoisomerism of this type is called "mirror-image" or "optical" isomerism because of the different actions of the isomers on polarised light which is discussed below.

The most common cause of a molecule being dissymmetric is that it contains one or more "asymmetric carbon atoms", that is, carbon atoms that are linked to four different groups. Only dissymmetric molecules of this type will be considered here. The fact that four different symmetrical

33

groups can be linked to a carbon atom in two ways to give two dissymmetric mirror-image molecules is readily grasped by building models such as the following:

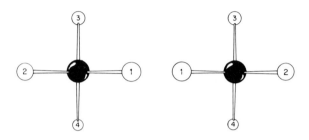

An example of such a compound with one asymmetric carbon atom is lactic acid. Two different models of this compound can be built that are mirror images of one another:

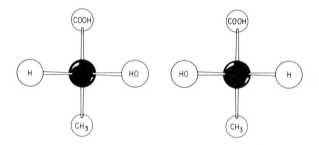

When synthesised in the laboratory lactic acid is in fact found to be a mixture of two isomers that can be separated by methods described later.

When a dissymmetric object interacts with a symmetrical object the consequences are always the same as when its mirror image interacts with the same object (except that one set of consequences may be the mirror image of the other); but when a dissymmetric object and its mirror image interact with the same dissymmetric object the consequences are quite different. This principle can be illustrated as follows. Suppose we have two bolts, one with a right-handed, and the other with a left-handed thread. We can push them into a close-fitting piece of rubber tubing with equal ease (although one may twirl clockwise as it enters, and the other an equal amount anticlockwise). But if we try to screw them into a nut made for the right-handed bolt, the right-handed bolt will enter easily whereas the left-handed bolt will strip the thread. This principle can be applied to enantiòmers such as the two forms of lactic acid. They react with symmetrical molecules at identical rates to give identical products (except that one may be the mirror image of the other). Thus the two enantiomers of lactic acid are oxidised at equal rates with potassium permanganate to give the same symmetrical product, pyruvic acid:

CH$_3$—C—COOH with H above and OH below (Lactic acid) → CH$_3$—C—COOH with O double bond below (Pyruvic acid)

Lactic acid   Pyruvic acid

They are also esterified with methanol at equal rates to give the two enantiomers of methyl lactate. Enantiomers also have identical melting and boiling points. But with dissymmetric molecules, notably enzymes, they react quite differently. Thus, the enzyme lactic dehydrogenase catalyses the oxidation of only one enantiomer of lactic acid to pyruvic acid.

Solutions of enantiomers can conveniently be distinguished from one another in a polarimeter by their effect on plane polarised light: they rotate the plane of polarisation in equal but opposite directions. If two solutions of equal strength of the two enantiomers of a dissymmetric compound such as lactic acid are put successively into the tube of a polarimeter it is found that with one enantiomer the plane of polarisation is rotated clockwise as seen by the operator (i.e., to the right at the top of the instrument), while with the other it is rotated through an equal angle in the opposite direction (i.e., to the left at the top). Hence, the two types of enantiomer were originally called *dextro* and *laevo* rotating respectively after the Latin for right and left, e.g., *dextro*- or (d)- lactic acid and *laevo*- or (l)- lactic acid. These terms have now been replaced by (+)- and (−)- respectively, e.g., (+)-lactic acid. The angle through which the plane of polarisation is rotated is characteristic of each compound. It is expressed as the specific rotation (α), which is the rotation in degrees of 1 gm of the substance per ml of solution in a tube 10 cm long. Thus the specific rotation of sucrose in aqueous solution is expressed as $(\alpha)_D^{20°} = +66.5°$ where D indicates the wave length as that of a sodium lamp and 20° indicates the temperature. Specific rotations are listed in tables of physical constants and are often useful in identifying optically active compounds.

It is at first sight perplexing how dissymmetric molecules in solution that are orientated in all directions can together have any effect on polarised light; that is, why the effect of a molecule pointing in one direction is not cancelled out by that of another pointing in the opposite direction. The reason is simply that a dissymmetric structure does not become its mirror image by rotation through 180°. The effect of dissymmetric molecules on polarised light can be illustrated by a simple analogy. Suppose we have two hollow pipes and pack one with small carpenters' screws with right-handed threads, and the other with similar screws with left-handed threads, the screws in both pipes being orientated in all directions. If we squirt water through each pipe it will emerge from one in a right-handed helix and from the other in a left-handed helix. The reason is that a screw has the same effect whether its point or its head is in the direction of flow. Similarly a corkscrew would still have to be inserted into a cork in a clockwise direction even if the handle were attached to the point, and the end previously attached to the handle driven into the cork.

2. Separation of Mirror-Image Molecules

The following are some further general features of dissymmetric objects. A dissymmetric object can only be made repeatedly, without also making the mirror-image object, by a dissymmetric agent. For example, a factory for making screws with right-handed threads must use a machine with a dissymmetric component; and another factory for making similar left-handed screws by a similar process must use a machine that is the mirror image of the first. There are two types of process by which dissymmetric objects can be made by symmetrical agents, but neither will repeatedly give one structure without its mirror image. In the first type of process the dissymmetric object is always produced together with its mirror image. An example would be the manufacture of pairs of gloves with symmetrical machinery as follows:

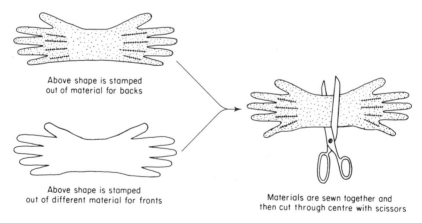

Above shape is stamped
out of material for backs

Above shape is stamped
out of different material for fronts

Materials are sewn together and
then cut through centre with scissors

In the second type of process a dissymmetric object is always produced alone, but it is a matter of chance which of the two mirror-image forms it will be. Hence, when the process is repeated many times the numbers of each form will be virtually the same. It is again possible to conceive of a symmetrical machine that would make right- and left-handed gloves in roughly equal numbers by inserting a thumb at random onto the right or left side of a symmetrical four-fingered precursor.

These principles can again be applied to chemistry. A particular dissymmetric molecule will only be made repeatedly without its enantiomer, by a dissymmetric agent, the most common dissymmetric agents being enzymes. Dissymmetric molecules can be formed in the laboratory from symmetrical precursors and reagents, as in the reduction of pyruvic acid to lactic acid with nascent hydrogen. But each time a molecule of pyruvic acid is reduced it is a matter of chance which of the two enantiomers of lactic acid is formed. Hence when large numbers of molecules are reduced the enantiomers are formed in virtually equal numbers. Such a mixture of enantiomers is known as a "racemic modification" (the term *racemic mixture* is now used to denote a mixture of separate crystals of the (+)-form and (−)-form which sometimes results on crystallising a racemic modification; the term *racemate* or *racemic compound* denotes crystals in which (+)- and (−)-enantiomers have paired to form a loose compound).

The separation of one pure enantiomer from a racemic modification is known as the "resolution" of the modification. In chemical syntheses of compounds with more than one asymmetric carbon, resolution must be carried out after every step that introduces an asymmetric carbon. It has been seen (p. 34) that a dissymmetric object will only behave differently from its mirror image in an encounter with another dissymmetric object. Since methods of resolution depend on treating one enantiomer differently to the other, all these methods use a dissymmetric agent. Methods of resolution are summarised below.

A. Separation of crystals

Occasionally racemic modifications will crystallise to give racemic mixtures in which the mirror-image crystals can be distinguished with a lens and separated with tweezers. The method is only of historical interest: Pasteur in 1848 performed the first resolution by separating the enantiomers of sodium ammonium tartrate in this way.

B. Seeding

If a saturated solution of a racemic modification is inoculated with a crystal of one of the enantiomers this may cause the same enantiomer to crystallise by itself. This method requires the prior existence of one enantiomer; but sometimes a different dissymmetric crystal will act as seed. Thus, (+)-sodium ammonium tartrate will crystallise from a solution of the racemic modification either on adding one of the same crystals, or a crystal of (−)-asparagine. This method is again little used, but it has been suggested that it occurred during the origin of life (see p. 50).

C. Formation of diastereoisomers

If the two enantiomers in a racemic modification both combine with one enantiomer of another dissymmetric compound to give two compounds each with two dissymmetric centers, these compounds are not mirror images. (They bear the same relation to one another that a right-handed black glove tied to a right-handed white glove bears to a left-handed black glove also tied to a right-handed white glove). Such compounds are called "diastereoisomers" and, for reasons discussed later (see p. 44), they differ in all their properties; this fact is made use of in resolving racemic modifications.

An example of this method was the resolution of the amino acid alanine by Emil Fischer. He first converted (±)-alanine to the (±)-benzoyl derivative in order to mask the amino group, but leave the carboxyl group free:

$$CH_3 \overset{\overset{\displaystyle H}{|}}{\underset{\underset{\displaystyle NH_2}{|}}{C}} COOH \longrightarrow CH_3 \overset{\overset{\displaystyle H}{|}}{\underset{\underset{\displaystyle NH.CO.C_6H_5}{|}}{C}} COOH$$

Alanine

He then allowed this acid to react with the organic base (−)-brucine to give salts that were diastereoisomers: the (−)-brucine salt of (+)-benzoyl-alanine and the (−)-brucine salt of (−)-benzoylalanine. Fischer separated the least soluble salt by crystallisation and, by removing the benzoyl group, obtained (−)-alanine. This is the method most commonly used for resolution during organic syntheses, and dissymmetric compounds are available that will react with acids, bases, alcohols, aldehydes, ketones, and other compounds. The diastereoisomers may be separated by many methods, including distillation and chromatrography, although fractional crystallisation usually works best.

D. Enzymic methods

Because enzymes are dissymmetric, when an enzyme catalyses a reaction of a dissymmetric compound, it rarely catalyses that of its enantiomer. Enzymes can therefore be used to remove one enantiomer from a racemic modification. Pasteur, in effect, used this method when he incubated the ammonium salt of (±)-tartaric acid with yeast. The yeast fermented the (+)-acid leaving its enantiomer. A more recent example of this method is the following convenient resolution of amino acids. The (±)-amino acid is first acetylated and the product then incubated with an acylase enzyme isolated from hog's kidney. Only the acetyl derivative of the naturally occurring amino acid is hydrolysed, and the resulting free amino acid may be isolated on a column of ion-exchange resin. The unchanged acetyl derivative of the enantiomer may be extracted with ethyl acetate and hydrolysed with acid. The following represents the resolution of (±)-alanine by this method:

$$CH_3—CH.COOH \qquad CH_3—CH.COOH \qquad \xrightarrow{(Acylase)} \qquad CH_3—CH.COOH$$

$$NH_2 \qquad\qquad\qquad NH \qquad\qquad\qquad\qquad NH_2$$

$$CO.CH_3$$

(±)-Alanine   (±)-Acetylalanine   (+)-Alanine

It has been seen that all methods of resolution require a dissymmetric agent. In (d) this agent is an enzyme, in (c) a dissymmetric compound and in (b) a dissymmetric crystal. In (a) the dissymmetric agent is less easy to pin down. The method involves a crystal acting on the brain of the operator. One kind of crystal produces a different result from its mirror image: the operator puts it in one beaker rather than in another. These different results must stem from some dissymmetric center in the operator's brain.

All methods of resolution are founded on the dissymmetry of living organisms. In method (d) the enzyme is derived from a living organism, while in (a) the operator is a living organism. If method (b) is to give the same enantiomer consistently, the correct one of two mirror-image crystals must first be selected by method (a). In method (c) the dissymmetric compound is either isolated from a living organism or obtained by methods such as (a), (b), or (d). How living organisms came to be dissymmetric is considered later (p. 50).

3. Absolute and Relative Configurations

It has been seen that two dissymmetric molecular models can be built of a compound that has one asymmetric carbon such as lactic acid: and such a compound does in fact exist in two forms whose similarities and differences are those that would be expected of mirror-image molecules. The problem that will now be considered is: given any two enantiomers and the corresponding two molecular models, which model corresponds to which enantiomer? For example, do the molecules of (+)-lactic acid have the structure of the model on the left or the right of p. 34? This is known as the problem of assigning absolute configurations.

Before discussing this problem some ways in which the structures of dissymmetric molecules are represented on paper will be described. One way of doing this is to draw a three-dimensional model as was done on p. 34 for each structure of lactic acid. But this is tedious, and chemists have devised more rapid conventions. The commonest of these is the use of "Fischer projection formulae". In these formulae asymmetric carbons are depicted with their four bonds at the points of the compass; but it is understood that the bonds pointing north and south in fact point below the plane of the paper, while those pointing east and west in fact point above it. Thus:

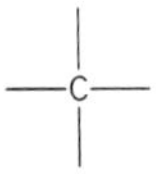

$$\overset{|}{\underset{|}{-C-}} \qquad \text{represents} \qquad$$

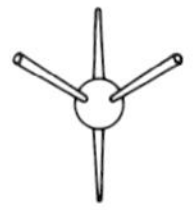

The two models of lactic acid on p. 34 are therefore drawn as:

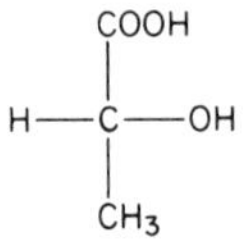

$$
\begin{array}{ccc}
\text{COOH} & & \text{COOH} \\
| & & | \\
\text{H}-\text{C}-\text{OH} & \text{and} & \text{HO}-\text{C}-\text{H} \\
| & & | \\
\text{CH}_3 & & \text{CH}_3
\end{array}
$$

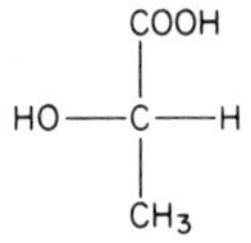

Correct molecular structures will still be deduced if these projection formulae are rotated through 180° thus:

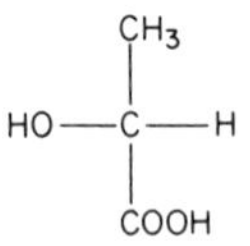

$$
\begin{array}{ccc}
\text{CH}_3 & & \text{CH}_3 \\
| & & | \\
\text{HO}-\text{C}-\text{H} & \text{and} & \text{H}-\text{C}-\text{OH} \\
| & & | \\
\text{COOH} & & \text{COOH}
\end{array}
$$

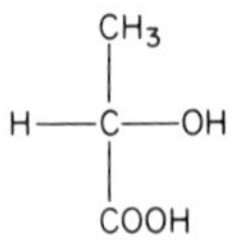

But if they are rotated through 90° the wrong structures will be deduced, since it will be concluded that groups which in fact point below the plane of the paper point above it. These facts are sometimes important in making deductions about the structure of certain molecules (e.g., see p. 44). Sometimes the orientation of the four bonds in projection formulae are indicated as:

$$\begin{array}{ccc}
\underset{CH_3}{\overset{COOH}{H-\!\!\!\!\blacksquare C\blacksquare\!\!\!\!-OH}} & \text{and} & \underset{CH_3}{\overset{COOH}{HO-\!\!\!\!\blacksquare C\blacksquare\!\!\!\!-H}}
\end{array}$$

Conventions have also been devised by which a particular dissymmetric molecular structure can be implied by putting a symbol before the name of a compound. The most familiar is the convention by which a particular one of the two mirror-image structures of a compound with one asymmetric carbon is referred to by the prefix D- or L-. This convention is applied to compounds of the structure $R-CHX-R'$ where X is a functional group and $R-C-R'$ is the main carbon chain of the molecule. If such a compound has the prefix D- then the correct Fischer projection formula can be deduced as follows. The asymmetric carbon is drawn with its bonds towards the points of the compass. The part of the main carbon chain that contains C_1 is placed to the north and the remainder of the chain to the south. (See p. 27 for conventions by which carbon chains are numbered). The hydrogen atom is then placed to the west (i.e., to the left) and the group X to the right. If the compound has the prefix L- the projection formula is drawn in the same way but with H- and X- interchanged. Thus:

$$\begin{array}{ccc}
\underset{R'}{\overset{R}{H-C-X}} & & \underset{R'}{\overset{R}{X-C-H}} \\
\text{D-Structure} & & \text{L-Structure}
\end{array}$$

Thus, the model on the left of p. 34 depicts D-lactic acid and that on the right depicts L-lactic acid. Similarly D-glyceraldehyde, L-alanine, D-malic acid and L-2-chloropentane imply, respectively, the following projection formulae:

$$\begin{array}{cccc}
\underset{CH_2OH}{\overset{CHO}{H-C-OH}} & \underset{CH_3}{\overset{COOH}{H_2N-C-H}} & \underset{CH_2.COOH}{\overset{COOH}{H-C-OH}} & \underset{C_3H_7}{\overset{CH_3}{Cl-C-H}}
\end{array}$$

The prefix D- or L- is sometimes given to a compound with more than one asymmetric carbon. It then refers to the configuration of one particular carbon specified by convention, as in the sugars (see p. 61).

The use of the letters D- and L- to denote a particular configuration is confusing since it wrongly suggests some relation to the *dextro-* or *laevo*-rotatory effect on polarised light. The reason that these letters are used is that the present convention evolved from older ones in which the configurations of compounds were first related to those of *dextro-* and *laevo*-rotatory glucose, and later to those of glyceraldehyde. To minimise the confusion, effects on polarised light are now designated (+)- and (−)- rather than (d)- and (l)- as formerly.

We can now return to the problem of assigning absolute configurations which, for the example of lactic acid, can now be reworded as: is (+)-lactic acid D- or L-lactic acid? The problem has proved difficult to solve and absolute configurations were assigned to the first two enantiomers only in 1951. It has been seen that any two enantiomers interact differently with the same dissymmetric object, and that they can be distinguished in this way. But to assign absolute configurations it is not only necessary to detect a difference between the enantiomers, but to deduce the particular configuration of each from the known structure of the dissymmetric object with which they interact. An analogy from everyday life may make this clearer. Suppose we were given a wooden board into which right- and left-handed screws had been screwed, and also given an electric screwdriver. We could distinguish between the two kinds of screw by switching on the screwdriver and finding which screws it would, and which it would not, unscrew. But we could only decide which had right-handed, and which left-handed, threads if we observed whether the screwdriver was rotating clockwise or anticlockwise.

The first successful attempt to deduce the configurations of enantiomers from their interactions with a dissymmetric agent was made in 1951 by the use of a special adaptation of X-ray diffraction. The absolute configurations that were assigned were those of (+)- and (−)-tartaric acids (see p. 48). A few other absolute configurations have since been assigned by X-ray diffraction. A few more have also been assigned by deducing theoretically which of two mirror-image structures under consideration should be (+)- and which (−)-rotating. There is however no simple relation between configuration and optical rotation and these deductions are difficult to make.

Once absolute configuration of a few enantiomers have been assigned, those of almost all others can be determined by discovering their "relative configurations". One method of determining the relative configuration of two dissymmetric compounds is to take one enantiomer of one compound and convert it into the other compound and discover which enantiomer is formed. Thus (+)-glyceraldehyde on oxidation gives (−)-glyceric acid. It may therefore be concluded that the aldehyde group in (+)-glyceraldehyde and the carboxyl group in (−)-glyceric acid bear the same spatial relationship to the remaining three groups on the asymmetric carbon. But unless the absolute configuration of one of these enantiomers is known it is impossible to assign them the correct molecular models. The relative configurations of these and many other compounds were discovered at a time when there appeared little chance of assigning any absolute configurations. Hence a guess was made as to the absolute configuration of (+)-glyceraldehyde and the configurations of other compounds were related to this. It was guessed that (+)-glyceraldehyde has the projection formula which we now name D-glyceraldehyde (see structure above).

Some more relative configurations are shown below, all Fischer projection formulae being drawn on the assumption that (+)-glyceraldehyde is D-glyceraldehyde:

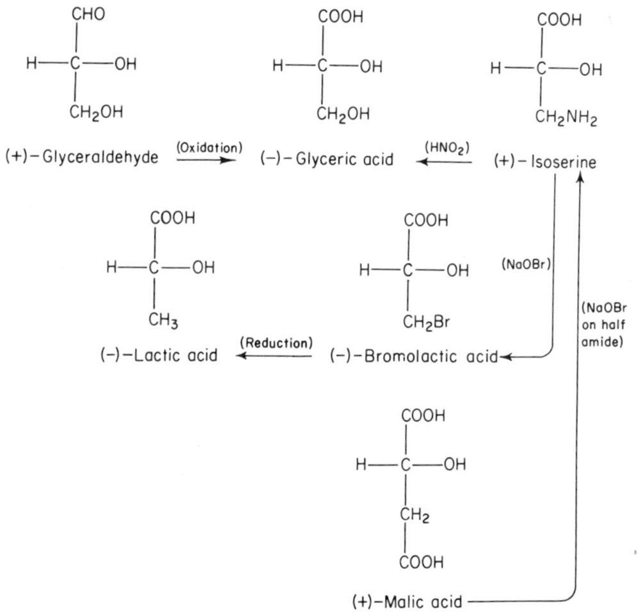

When relative configurations are determined in this way it is essential that the four bonds from the asymmetric carbon to the four adjacent atoms are never broken—the chemical conversion must involve groups which are away from the asymmetric centre. The reason for this is that when a bond from an asymmetric carbon is broken in a reaction which gives an asymmetric product, an "inversion" of configuration often occurs. In a reaction in which a group e is replaced by f this may be represented as:

Other methods are also available for assigning relative configurations.

In fact, only relative configurations are important to the organic chemist since he is only concerned with the relation between one enantiomer and another in chemical conversions. He need not worry if the whole of his conception of organic chemistry is the mirror image of the truth! However, the absolute configurations that have been determined show that the configuration of (+)-glyceraldehyde was guessed correctly. Hence the chemist's conception of molecular structure is the true one, and not its mirror image. Thus, (+)-tartaric acid, whose absolute configuration was proved to be that shown below, gives (+)-malic acid on reduction:

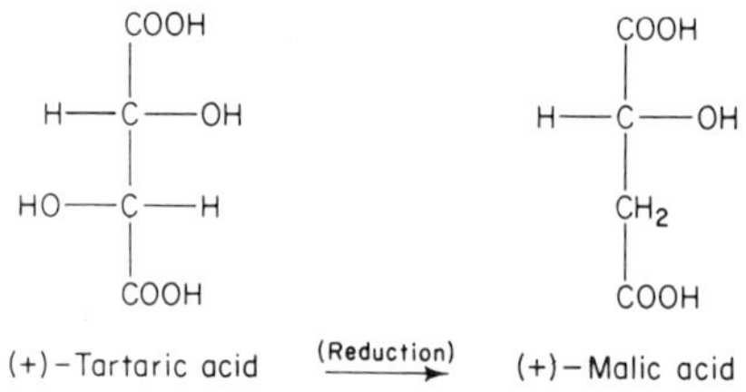

(+)-Tartaric acid $\xrightarrow{\text{(Reduction)}}$ (+)-Malic acid

[It should be noted that whereas tartaric acid has two asymmetric carbons (see p. 48), malic acid has only one. The same enantiomer of malic acid is formed whichever hydroxyl of (+)-tartaric acid is reduced as may be proved by rotating the projection formulae through 180° (see p. 40)]. Since the projection formula of (+)-tartaric acid shown above is correct, that of (+)-malic acid is also correct. Hence all the projection formulae in the conversions outlined above, including that of (+)-glyceraldehyde, are also correct.

4. Molecules With More Than One Asymmetric Carbon

If a compound has more than one asymmetric carbon atom it has optical isomers of two kinds: an enantiomer with the mirror-image configuration on each of the asymmetric carbons, and also isomers, known as "diastereoisomers", which have the mirror-image configuration on some of the asymmetric carbons, but the same configuration on others. While any pair of enantiomers differ from one another only in their interactions with dissymmetric objects, diastereoisomers also differ in interactions with symmetrical objects, as explained below, and hence differ in all their chemical and physical properties. Diastereoisomers can be illustrated by the aldose sugars (see p. 57). These are compounds in which an aldehyde group is attached to a chain of carbon atoms, each of which bears a hydroxyl group.

Glyceraldehyde or glycerose is an aldose, and since it has three carbon atoms it is called an aldotriose. It has only one asymmetric carbon, and hence has only one optical isomer which is its enantiomer. Next in the series of aldoses come aldotetroses which all have the structure:

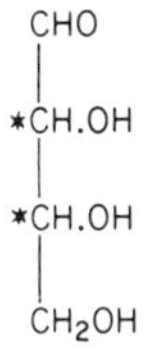

$$
\begin{array}{c}
\text{CHO} \\
| \\
*\text{CH.OH} \\
| \\
*\text{CH.OH} \\
| \\
\text{CH}_2\text{OH}
\end{array}
$$

The two carbons marked with an asterisk are asymmetric: each is linked to four different groups which can be arranged around the carbon in two ways to give structures that are mirror images of one another. Four isomers therefore result from combining these structures together in all possible ways. Their Fischer projection formulae are:

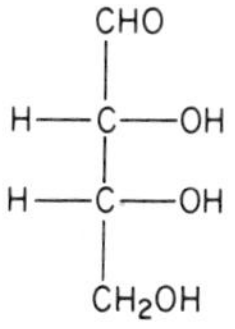

CHO	CHO	CHO	CHO
H—C—OH	HO—C—H	HO—C—H	H—C—OH
H—C—OH	HO—C—H	H—C—OH	HO—C—H
CH₂OH	CH₂OH	CH₂OH	CH₂OH
1a	1b	2a	2b

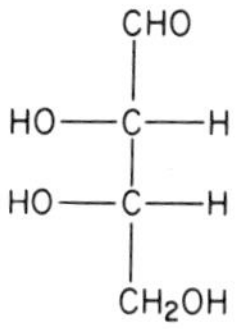

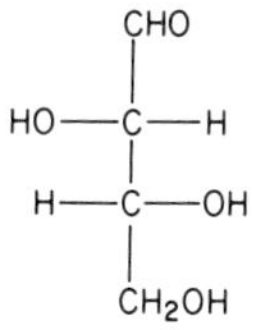

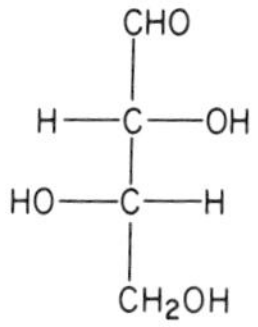

(When deducing the orientation of bonds from Fischer projection formulae with more than one asymmetric carbon, each of these carbons must be considered separately. Thus, the above projection formulae imply that with both C_2 and C_3 the bonds to the north and south are directed below the paper, and those to the east and west above it). The situation is similar to the fact that either one of a pair of white gloves can be tied to either one of a pair of black gloves to give four different combinations:

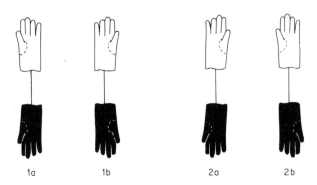

In the above projection formulae of the aldotetroses it is seen that the —OH groups are adjacent in 1(a) and 1(b) and opposed in 2(a) and 2(b). It is important to realise that this is not a permanent state of affairs as it is between the carboxyls of fumaric and maleic acids (see p. 18). Because the asymmetric carbons are joined by a single bond, they can rotate freely relative to one another, and the —OH groups have merely been arranged in this way to meet the requirements of Fischer projection formulae, as is seen clearly in molecular models:

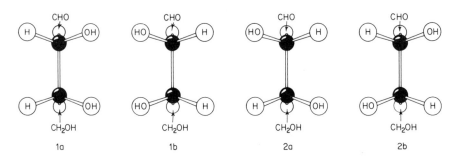

These molecules are in an eclipsed conformation whereas in reality they must largely exist in one of the more stable staggered conformations (see p. 12). For this and other reasons different projection formulae are sometimes used for compounds with more than one asymmetric carbon. These are "sawhorse" formulae which give a three-dimensional view of the molecule, and "Newman formulae" which show the relative positions of the groups when viewed from one end of the molecule. Sawhorse and Newman formulae for one of the staggered conformations of each of the aldotetroses are shown below:

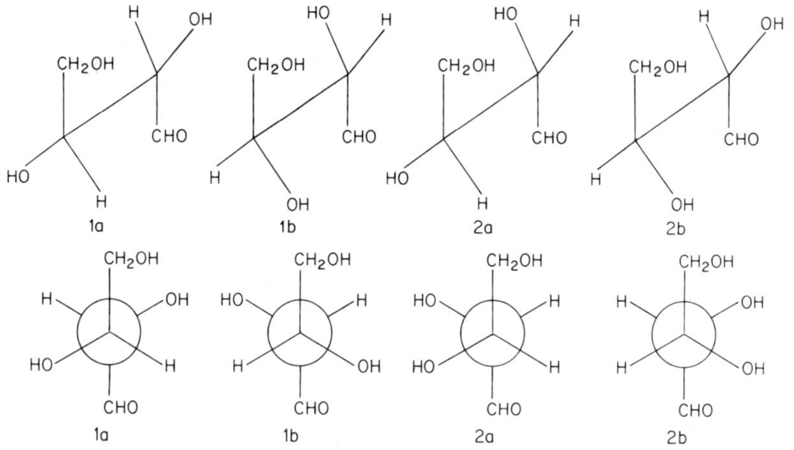

The molecules of the aldotetroses 1(a) and 1(b) as represented in all the above formulae are mirror images of one another. Because there is free rotation between the asymmetric carbon atoms, two molecules of structure 1(a) and 1(b) will not at every instant be mirror images of one another. But each of a large number of molecules of structure 1(a) will have its mirror image in one of a large number of molecules of structure 1(b). Hence aldotetroses 1(a) and 1(b) are enantiomers, and the same is true of aldotetroses 2(a) and 2(b). But molecules 1(a) and 1(b) each have one carbon of identical configuration to one of the carbons of 2(a) or 2(b) and one of different configuration. Therefore, neither 1(a) nor 1(b) can assume structures that are the mirror images of 2(a) or 2(b). As a result 1(a) and 1(b) differ from their "diastereoisomers" 2(a) and 2(b) in interactions with both dissymmetric and symmetrical objects, and so differ in all their chemical and physical properties. For this reason diastereoisomers are given different names. The aldotetroses are named erythrose and threose. (How it is proved which of the above four structures is that of (+)-erythrose, (−)-erythrose, (+)-threose and (−)-threose is discussed in the next chapter.)

The fact that two diastereoisomers will differ in all their chemical and physical properties can be further understood as follows. Although any two diastereoisomers have the same component atoms joined by identical covalent bonds, all distances between corresponding atoms are never the same in the two molecules. This is clearly shown in the above Newman projection formulae of the aldotetroses. These show the staggered conformations in which the —CH$_2$OH and —CHO groups are at the maximum, and the same, distance apart in all four molecules. It is seen that in 1(a) and 1(b) the —OH groups are also at the maximum distance apart, as are the —H atoms, whereas in 2(a) and 2(b) this is not so. As a result, interactomic forces in the diastereoisomers will differ, and hence their chemical and physical properties will differ. That these differences include reactions with symmetrical molecules can be illustrated as follows. A symmetrical object can never be placed in turn beside each of two diastereoisomers, so that the distances between the component atoms and the component parts of the object are identical with each diastereoisomer. Thus, if a square object is held vertically above 1(a) or 1(b), opposite corners of the square will lie above —OH groups. If it is held above 2(a) or 2(b) adjacent corners will lie above —OH groups. Hence if the symmetrical object is an approaching molecule the intermolecular forces between it and (1a) or 1(b) will differ from those between it and 2(a) or 2(b). Hence the chemical reactions will differ.

Conversely, all distances between corresponding atoms in two enantiomers are identical. The distances between their component atoms and the component parts of another object will always differ only if this object is dissymmetric. Thus, if a square is held over 1(a) or 1(b) two opposite corners of the square will lie above —OH groups, the other two corners above —H atoms, and opposite sides above —CH$_2$OH and —CHO groups. But if the palm of the right hand is held above 1(a), with the forefinger above the —CH$_2$OH group, then the —OH on the nearest asymmetric carbon will lie below the thumb, and the hydrogen below the little finger. If the forefinger of the same hand is next placed above the same group in 1(b), then the —OH now lies below the little finger and the —H below the thumb.

It has been seen that a compound with one asymmetric carbon has one optical isomer which is its enantiomer; and a compound with two different asymmetric carbons has one enantiomer and two diastereoisomers that are enantiomers of one another. In general, when a compound has n different asymmetric carbons, it and its optical isomers number 2^n. There are $\frac{2^n}{2}$ pairs of enantiomers. The members of each pair are diastereoisomers of all the other pairs, and differ from them in all their properties. Hence, each pair of enantiomers is usually given a distinct chemical name. Examples of such compounds are the aldopentoses and aldohexoses (see p. 61).

Special instances of compounds with two asymmetric carbon atoms are those in which each carbon is attached to the same four groups. Such a compound is tartaric acid in which the four groups are —H, —OH,

—COOH and —C·H·OH·COOH. The following are four projection formulae for tartaric acid corresponding to those of the aldotetroses given above:

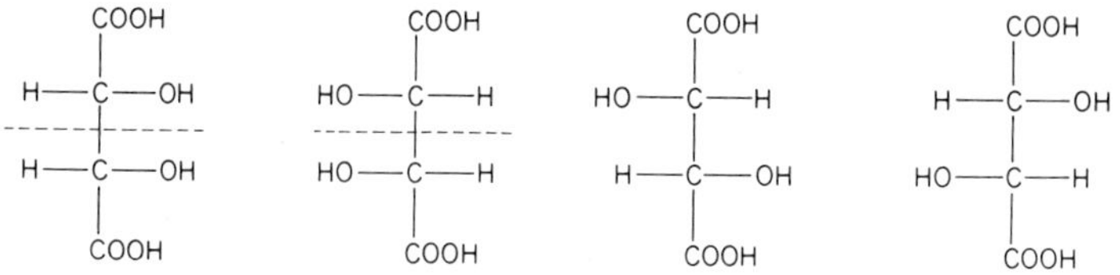

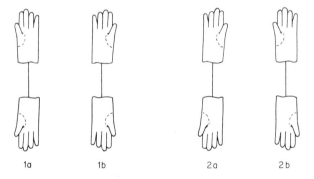

It is seen that enantiomers 1(a) and 1(b) are identical and have a plane of symmetry, shown by the dotted line. The identity of 1(a) and 1(b) is also proved by rotating one of the projection formulae through 180° (see p. 40). The situation is the same as if we had two pairs of identical gloves and joined two gloves together in all possible ways:

Again 1(a) and 1(b) are identical and have a plane of symmetry between the two gloves. As expected from the identity of 1(a) and 1(b) only three optical isomers of tartaric acid are known. They are (+)- and (−)-tartaric acids which are enantiomers, and an isomer which is their diastereoisomer and is optically inactive and hence must have a plane of symmetry. Although, as expected, it differs from the enantiomers in all its properties (it is less dense, less soluble in water, and a weaker acid) and should systematically be given a different name, it is in fact called *meso*-tartaric acid. (The prefix *meso*- is given to compounds which are symmetrical owing to the dissymmetry of one part of the molecule being balanced by that of another part.)

5. The Origin of Dissymmetry in Living Organisms

Many living organisms have dissymmetric structures that are not balanced by mirror-image structures in the way that a man's right hand is balanced by his left. A particularly interesting example is the helical shell of the snail *Limnaea peregra* which may be coiled in a right-handed helix (i.e., like a normal corkscrew) or in a left-handed one:

Strains of these snails can be selected that will always breed progeny with right-handed shells, or with left-handed shells. In accordance with the general principles that govern the formation of dissymmetric objects (see p. 36) these two kinds of shell must be produced by two different dissymmetric agents. (By the same principles, dissymetric structures like hands that are accompanied by equal numbers of mirror-image structures need not be produced by a dissymmetric agent.)

If the development of the snails is followed it is found that the direction of coiling of the shell is determined by a right- or left-handed orientation of the spindle at the second cleavage division of the fertilised egg. Chemical genetics enables an intelligent guess to be made as to which agents, in turn, determine the dissymmetry of the spindle. It has been found that the coiling of the shell is determined by a single pair of alleles, the right-handed shell being dominant over the left-handed.

Chemical genetics has shown that a gene acts by directing the formation of a protein of a specific amino acid sequence which is determined by the nucleotide sequence of the DNA of the gene. Differences between genes are founded on differences in nucleotide sequence, and hence different genes direct the formation of proteins of different amino acid sequence. The dominant and recessive genes of this snail must differ slightly in the nucleotide sequence of their DNA, and hence they must direct the formation of proteins of slightly different amino acid sequence. It seems most probable that these proteins determine the dissymmetry of the spindle. It has been found that the molecules of many pure globular proteins assemble spontaneously into helixes which are stabilised by non-covalent forces between the molecules. Some of these helixes are left-handed and others right-handed, and it follows that whether the helix is right- or left-handed depends on the amino acid sequence of the protein. Hence, a change in amino acid sequence as the result of mutation might

50

well cause molecules that previously assembled into a right-handed helix, to assemble into a left-handed one.

Whatever is in fact the precise mechanism, the dissymmetry of this snail's shell must ultimately be a consequence of its genetic DNA being composed of dissymmetric molecules which are unaccompanied by their enantiomers. The same must be true of other unbalanced dissymmetric structures in living organisms of which there are many examples. It must also be true of a man's ability to taste the difference between enantiomers such as D- and L-glutamic acid. His taste buds must have dissymmetric molecules, whose structure is determined by the genetic DNA, and these must send different nervous stimuli to the brain when they interact with the different enantiomers. The same must also be true of a man's ability to discriminate between an object and its mirror image: the discrimination must occur at a dissymmetric centre in the brain whose dissymmetry depends on that of its component molecules, whose synthesis is in turn directed by inherited DNA.

At the molecular level unbalanced dissymmetry in living organisms is even more evident, almost every dissymmetric molecule occuring without its enantiomer: D-glucose without L-, L-alanine without D-, etc. This dissymmetry has been preserved through the ages by the passage of dissymmetric molecules from generation to generation in the germ cells, the most important molecules being those of DNA which apparently control the formation of all other molecules of cells. The problem remains of how dissymmetric molecules became separated from their enantiomers when life began. It is probable that life originated by the interaction of organic compounds produced by the action of radiations or electric discharges on methane, ammonia, and water vapour. In fact, in the laboratory, if an electric discharge is passed for some days through a globe containing these compounds, many of the compounds of living organisms are formed, including at least fourteen amino acids and various peptides. Dissymmetric compounds are however always formed as racemic modifications. The vital step in the origin of life lies between these molecules and a larger grouping of molecules which could form self copies at the expense of the molecules that surround it. In order for such a grouping to form self copies, dissymmetric molecules would amost certainly have to be present without their enantiomers, and the most probable way in which this would come about would seem to be by chance: a certain grouping of molecules capable of self-copying, and hence able to outnumber all competing groupings, would by chance be formed before the mirror-image grouping. If this is correct, then if life has originated in the same way on a number of planets, roughly half of the organisms formed will be composed of molecules which are the enantiomers of our own.

An alternative suggestion has been made that life originated in a localised concentration of one enantiomer of a dissymmetric compound which might have arisen in one of a number of ways. When enantiomers have different crystalline forms, one may crystallise spontaneously from a saturated solution of a racemic modification. This crystallisation may also sometimes be induced by a dissymmetric crystal of another compound. Dissymmetric crystals can also catalyse some asymmetric syntheses (see below). Quartz could possibly have provided the dissymmetric crystal: although quartz is composed of symmetrical molecules of silicon dioxide it crystallises into dissymmetric crystals, the two mirror-image forms being formed with equal probability. Asymmetric synthesis can also occur under the influence of polarised light, and sunlight reflected from the sea is slightly polarised.

6. Synthesis of Dissymmetric Molecules by Enzymes

It has been mentioned that a dissymmetric object can only be made repeatedly, without the mirror-image object, if a dissymmetric agent is used. In biochemical reactions when a dissymmetric compound is formed from a symmetrical one, one enantiomer is almost always formed to the exclusion of the other. Since almost all biochemical reactions are catalysed by enzymes, which are dissymmetric proteins, this fact is in accordance with the general principles of dissymmetry. But it is important to analyse in detail the biochemical conversion of a symmetrical compound to a dissymmetric one. Failure to do so led in the 1940's to a basic misunderstanding of the tricarboxylic acid cycle which will be mentioned later.

The conversion of a symmetrical to an asymmetric carbon in one step may be represented:

$$
\begin{array}{ccc}
\underset{\underset{a}{|}}{\overset{\overset{a}{|}}{b-C-d}} \longrightarrow \underset{\underset{e}{|}}{\overset{\overset{a}{|}}{b-C-d}} & \text{or} & \underset{\underset{d}{|}}{\overset{\overset{b}{|}}{C=a}} \longrightarrow \underset{\underset{d}{|}}{\overset{\overset{b}{|}}{e-C-f}}
\end{array}
$$

Two bonds of the symmetrical carbon are linked to identical groups, or to the same group, while the remaining two are linked to two other different groups. Carbon atoms with this type of bonding have been named *meso* carbon atoms by biochemists. Biochemical examples of such conversions are the conversion of glycerol to L-α-glycerophosphate catalysed by glycerokinase of liver:

$$CH_2OH \qquad\qquad CH_2OH$$
$$HO-C-H \longrightarrow HO-C-H$$
$$CH_2OH \qquad\qquad CH_2OPO_3H_2$$

and the conversion of pyruvic acid to L-lactic acid catalysed by lactic dehydrogenase of muscle:

$$CHO \qquad\qquad COOH$$
$$C=O \longrightarrow HO-C-H$$
$$CH_3 \qquad\qquad CH_3$$

If one enantiomer is to be formed to the exclusion of the other, as occurs in these biochemical reactions, one of the a groups (or C—a bonds) must consistently react differently from the other. At first it is hard to see how this can happen, since they appear to be identical in every way. In fact, however, they differ in their positions relative to the other groups attached to the carbon, and they can be distinguished by a dissymmetric (but not a symmetrical) agent. This fact can be demonstrated most simply by laying a model of a *meso* carbon (C·a·a·b·d) on three circles, marked a, b, and d, arranged in a triangle. It is found that all the correct groups can only be placed on the correct circles when a particular one of the two a groups lies on the circle marked a:

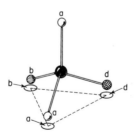

This dissymmetric pattern can thus distinguish between the two a groups. No symmetrical pattern will do so.

It is also possible to distinguish by eye between the two identical groups on a *meso* carbon. For example, a particular one of these two groups could always be selected by orientating the molecule $C·a·a·b·d$ with b and d to the north and south respectively, and pointing downwards. The a groups will then rise upwards and one will point east and the other west:

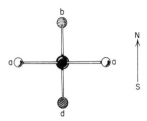

The two *a* groups are analogous to two identical horns protruding from the right and left sides of an animal's head. Although these are identical in structure they differ in their positions relative to other parts of the body.

An enzyme reacts differently with the two similar groups on a *meso* carbon because the interatomic distances and forces between these two groups and the groups on the dissymmetric enzyme are not identical. Experiments with isotopic tracers have shown that enzymes treat the two similar groups on a *meso* carbon in different ways even in a reaction which does not form an asymmetric carbon. For example, the enzyme alcohol dehydrogenase of yeast will catalyse the reduction of acetaldehyde to ethanol by reduced nicotine adenine dinucleotide. If the aldehyde group is labelled with ^{2}H, labelled ethanol is formed:

$$H_3C-C\diagdown{}^{O}_{^2H} \longrightarrow H_3C-\overset{\overset{\displaystyle H}{|}}{\underset{\underset{\displaystyle ^2H}{|}}{C}}-OH$$

This ethanol may be reoxidised to acetaldehyde by oxidised nicotine adenine dinucleotide in the presence of the same enzyme. It is found that all the ^{2}H in the ethanol is recovered in the acetaldehyde. Hence, when acetaldehyde is reduced, a particular one of the two C=O bonds becomes C—OH while the other becomes C—H; and it is this C—H bond from which hydrogen is removed when the ethanol is rexodised, and not the other (which in this experiment is labelled with ^{2}H). These results cannot be attributed to the abnormal presence of ^{2}H and it is clear that the two C=O bonds in acetaldehyde and the two C—H bonds in ethanol are always treated differently by this enzyme.

Failure to understand these principles led in the 1940's to a misinterpretation of experiments relating to the tricarboxylic acid cycle. H. A. Krebs had suggested that the initial reactions of the cycle are essentially as follows:

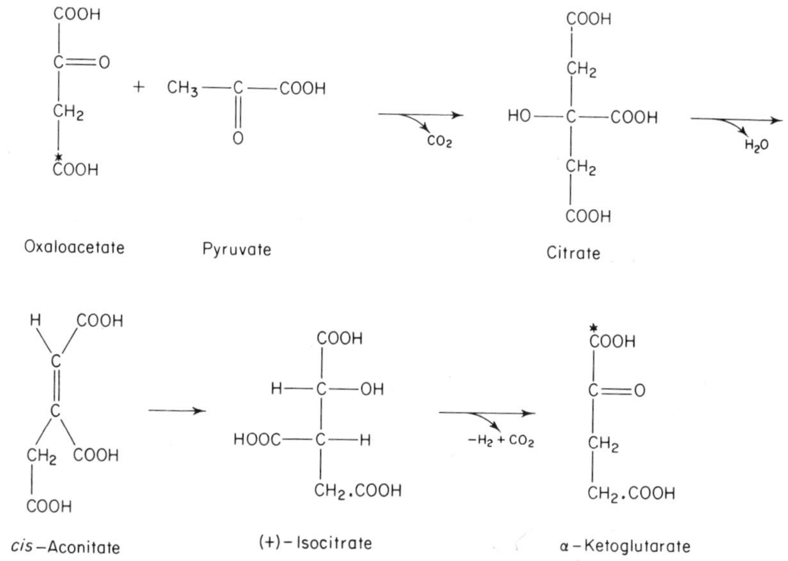

However, experiments were published in 1941 which, it was generally agreed, showed that this series of reactions was not entirely correct. In effect, oxaloacetate, labelled with isotopic carbon in the carboxyl adjacent to the CH_2 group (asterisked above), had been incubated with pigeon's liver, and α-ketoglutarate had later been isolated. It was found to be labelled only in the carboxyl adjacent to the carbonyl group (asterisked above). This result, it was concluded, showed that citrate could not be an intermediate in the conversion of oxaloacetate to ketoglutarate. The reason given was the following. Only one of the two —$CH_2 \cdot COOH$ groups of citrate would have become labelled; but since these groups are "identical" whenever a molecule reacted further there would be an equal chance of the unlabelled group becoming the —$CO \cdot COOH$ group of ketoglutarate as of the labelled. Hence, instead of only one carboxyl of ketoglutarate becoming labelled, both would have become labelled to the same extent.

This argument was accepted by all biochemists, and Krebs eliminated citrate from the cycle and renamed it the "tricarboxylic acid cycle". He suggested that oxaloacetate was converted directly to aconitate, so giving a series of dissymmetric compounds between oxaloacetate and ketoglutarate. Since citrate was certainly formed from oxaloacetate and pyruvate under certain conditions, he suggested that citrate could be formed from, and hence could itself give rise to, aconitate. To counter the objection that the presence of citrate on this epicycle would cause even distribution of labelled carbon between the carboxyls of ketoglutarate just as surely as if citrate lay on the cycle itself, Krebs marshalled evidence of the relative reaction rates; and he silenced all criticism with the unanswerable argument: "It is the only available hypothesis which satisfactorily explains the facts".

Not until 1948 did someone realise that the facts can be explained by another hypothesis which, like most theoretical advances, seems obvious in retrospect. A. G. Ogston pointed out that the two "identical" groups in citrate could be distinguished by an enzyme in the manner discussed above, and the following experiments soon proved that they are treated differently in the conversion of citrate to ketoglutarate. The incubation of pyruvate and labelled oxaloacetate with liver, which had yielded labelled ketoglutarate, was repeated, but under conditions in which citrate accumulated. This citrate was isolated. Ordinary chemical reagents, which cannot distinguish between the two —$CH_2 \cdot COOH$ groups, would have shown the label to be evenly distributed between these two groups of the citrate. But when this citrate was incubated with a fresh liver preparation, under conditions in which ketoglutarate accumulates, the label was again found to be solely in the carboxyl adjacent to the carbonyl group of ketoglutarate. These experiments showed that citrate could lie on the cycle; isolation of the enzyme by which citrate is formed showed that it does.

FURTHER READING

E. L. Eliel, *Stereochemistry of Carbon Compounds*, McGraw-Hill, New York, 1962.

Chapter 3

Carbohydrates

1. Open-Chain Structures of Monosaccharides

Carbohydrates are important components of living organisms. They received their name from the fact that they mostly have the common molecular formula Cx(H$_2$O)y. They may be divided into monosaccharides and their condensation products the oligosaccharides and polysaccharides. Monosaccharides and oligosaccharides are crystalline compounds, soluble in water and with a sweet taste. They are known as sugars. The polysaccharides have high molecular weights and do not taste sweet. Monosaccharides may be divided into trioses, tetroses, pentoses, hexoses, and heptoses according to the number of carbon atoms per molecule.

In solution a monosaccharide exists in two kinds of structure in equilibrium. In one, an aldehyde or ketone group forms part of a chain of saturated carbon atoms to each of which is normally attached a hydroxyl group. Examples are the aldohexose D(+)-glucose and the ketohexose D(−)-fructose:

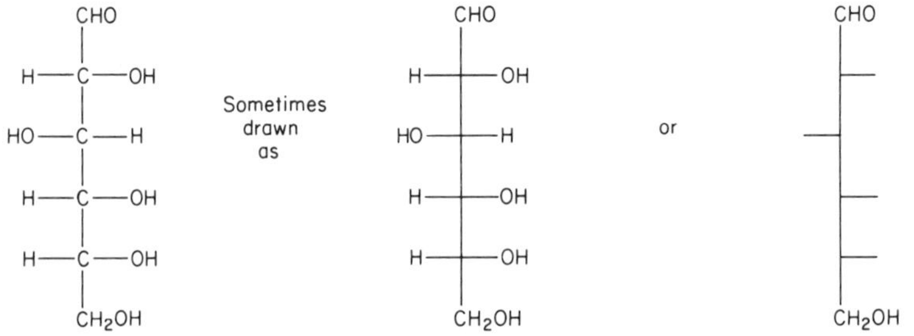

CHO
H—C—OH
HO—C—H   Sometimes drawn as
H—C—OH
H—C—OH
CH₂OH

D (+)–Glucose

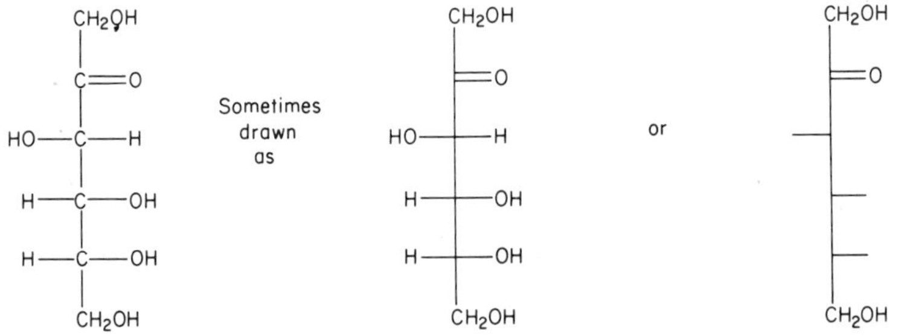

CHO
H———OH
HO———H   or
H———OH
H———OH
CH₂OH

CHO
|
|
|
|
CH₂OH

CH_2OH
C=O
HO—C—H   Sometimes drawn as
H—C—OH
H—C—OH
CH₂OH

D (–)–Fructose

CH₂OH
=O
HO———H   or
H———OH
H———OH
CH₂OH

CH₂OH
=O
|
|
|
CH₂OH

In equilibrium with molecules of this kind are others in which the aldehyde or ketone group has reacted with one of the hydroxyl groups in the same molecule to form a ring of five or six atoms. In solutions of some sugars, such as fructose, traces of open-chain molecules can be detected spectroscopically, but the vast majority of the molecules are rings, and in crystalline sugars they all are. It is simplest, however, to consider first the open-chain structures of the sugars, and many of the reactions of sugars in solution are in fact reactions of this form. The structure of sugar rings will be considered in the next section.

Most monosaccharides contain more than one asymmetric carbon per molecule and hence diastereoisomers occur (see p. 44). D-Glucose, for example, has four asymmetric carbons and in addition to the mirror-image L-glucose, it has seven pairs of diastereoisomers which are the other aldohexoses (D- and L-mannose, D- and L-galactose, etc). But before this diastereoisomerism is considered the manner in which the atoms are linked together will be proved. This linking in aldohexoses such as glucose is proved as follows:

(1) Elementary analyses and molecular weight determinations prove that they all have the molecular formula $C_6H_{12}O_6$.

(2) They will react with hydrogen cyanide to form cyanhydrins, a characteristic of aldehydes and ketones.

(3) On hydrolysis the cyanhydrin yields a carboxylic acid that will form a hexacetate, proving that it has six hydroxyl groups. On reduction of the carboxylic acid with hydriodic acid and red phosphorus, heptanoic acid is formed. From the known structure of this compound the reactions may be traced back to prove the structure of the aldohexoses:

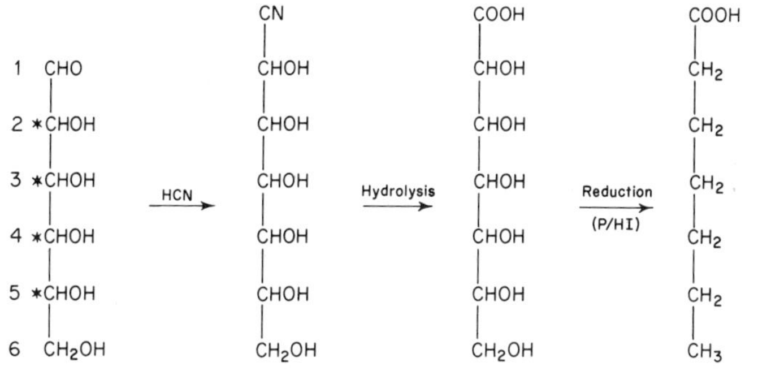

$$
\begin{array}{cccccccc}
 & & & CN & & COOH & & COOH \\
1 & CHO & & CHOH & & CHOH & & CH_2 \\
2 & *CHOH & & CHOH & & CHOH & & CH_2 \\
3 & *CHOH & \xrightarrow{HCN} & CHOH & \xrightarrow{Hydrolysis} & CHOH & \xrightarrow[(P/HI)]{Reduction} & CH_2 \\
4 & *CHOH & & CHOH & & CHOH & & CH_2 \\
5 & *CHOH & & CHOH & & CHOH & & CH_2 \\
6 & CH_2OH & & CH_2OH & & CH_2OH & & CH_3 \\
 & Aldohexose & & Cyanhydrin & & & & Heptanoic\ acid
\end{array}
$$

(The aldehyde group in aldoses is known as C_1 and the remaining carbons are numbered successively as shown.) The component atoms are thus similarly linked in all aldohexoses; they differ from one another in the arrangement of groups about asymmetric carbon atoms. By similar reactions the aldopentoses and aldotetroses can be proved to have the structures:

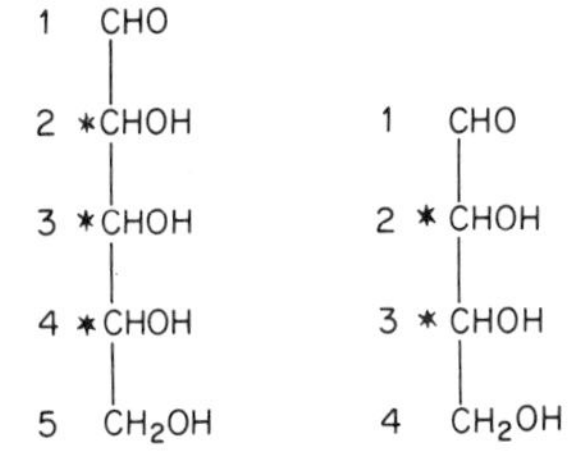

$$
\begin{array}{ll}
1 \quad CHO & \\
2 \quad *CHOH & 1 \quad CHO \\
3 \quad *CHOH & 2 \quad *CHOH \\
4 \quad *CHOH & 3 \quad *CHOH \\
5 \quad CH_2OH & 4 \quad CH_2OH \\
\text{Aldopentose} & \text{Aldotetrose}
\end{array}
$$

The naturally occurring ketohexoses give similar results in (a), (b) and (c) above, except that reduction of the carboxylic acid formed from the cyanhydrin yields 2-methylhexanoic acid. Hence the open-chain structure is:

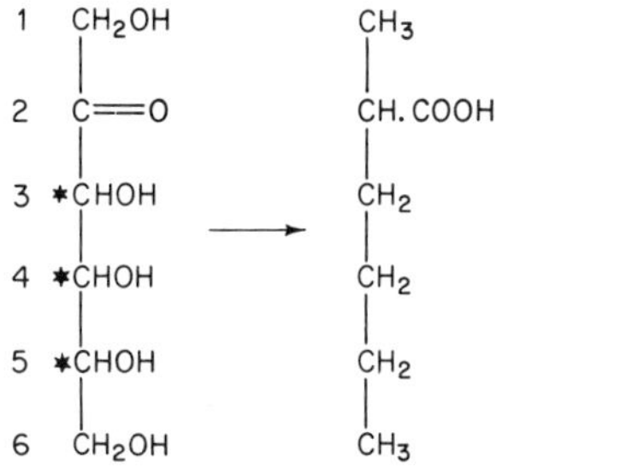

$$
\begin{array}{lll}
1 & CH_2OH & CH_3 \\
2 & C{=\!\!=}O & CH.COOH \\
3 & *CHOH & CH_2 \\
4 & *CHOH & \longrightarrow \quad CH_2 \\
5 & *CHOH & CH_2 \\
6 & CH_2OH & CH_3 \\
 & \text{Ketohexose} & \text{2- Methylhexanoic acid}
\end{array}
$$

(In ketoses, C_1 is always the terminal carbon nearest the ketone group as shown.)

Asymmetric carbons in the above formulae have been marked with asterisks. A molecule with n asymmetric carbons can exist in 2^n structures made up of $\frac{2^n}{2}$ enantiomeric (mirror-image) pairs of diastereoisomers (see p. 48). Hence, aldotetroses exist in $\frac{2^2}{2} = 2$ pairs of diastereoisomers; aldopentoses in $\frac{2^3}{2} = 4$ pairs of diastereoisomers; and aldohexoses in $\frac{2^4}{2} = 8$ pairs of diastereoisomers. The members of each of these pairs (e.g., (+)- and (−)-glucose) have identical properties except in their interactions with dissymmetric agents. But the properties of one pair of diastereoisomers differ in general from those of another. The different pairs are, therefore, given different names, such as glucose, mannose, galactose.

Shown below are the projection formulae of one enantiomer of each aldotetrose, aldopentose and aldohexose. (The particular sugar which possesses each of these structures has been written below it in anticipation of assignments made later):

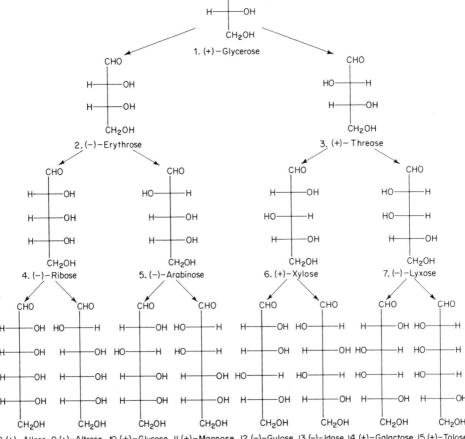

It must be remembered that each of these structures is the representation on paper, according to rules laid down by Fischer (see p. 40), of a particular molecular model predicted by stereochemical theory.

The convention by which the two predicted mirror-image structures of a compound with one asymmetric carbon are distinguished by the prefix D- or L- was explained earlier (see page 41). This convention is extended to sugars by considering only the asymmetric carbon adjacent to the terminal —CH_2OH group. If, in the Fischer projection formula, the hydrogen on this carbon is to the left and the hydroxyl to the right the structure is given the prefix D-; if the reverse, it is given the prefix L-. It is seen that all the structures in Figure 3 are those of D-sugars; each one has an L-enantiomer with the mirror-image configuration on *each* asymmetric carbon. Hence L-glucose is:

$$
\begin{array}{c}
\text{CHO} \\
\text{HO}\!-\!\!\!-\!\!\!-\!\text{H} \\
\text{H}\!-\!\!\!-\!\!\!-\!\text{OH} \\
\text{HO}\!-\!\!\!-\!\!\!-\!\text{H} \\
\text{HO}\!-\!\!\!-\!\!\!-\!\text{H} \\
\text{CH}_2\text{OH}
\end{array}
$$

Sugars were designated D- and L- in this way because they may be considered as built up from D- or L-glyceraldehyde (glycerose) by replacing the aldehyde group by a longer chain.

The final problem in proving the open-chain structures of sugars is therefore the following. Stereochemical theory predicts that two pairs of aldotetroses, four pairs of aldopentoses, and eight pairs of aldohexoses should exist, the members of each pair being distinguished by the prefix D- or L-; and all these pairs of sugars have in fact been synthesised or isolated from natural sources, the members of each pair having equal but opposite specific rotations and accordingly being distinguished by the prefix (+)- or (−)-. How is each sugar assigned to one of the predicted structures? These assignments were made over a number of years from fragments of evidence largely discovered by Fischer. In retrospect, neater series of proofs can be devised, and one of these is given below.

One of the most important reactions used in this assignment of configurations to sugars is the Kiliani synthesis, which provides a general way of converting an aldose to two higher aldoses, with one more carbon in the chain. The aldose is converted to its cyanhydrin, the cyanide group of which is then hydrolysed to carboxyl. The resulting acid is converted by heating to its anhydride, which is then reduced. Two sugars, which are diastereoisomers, result because an additional asymmetric carbon has been introduced:

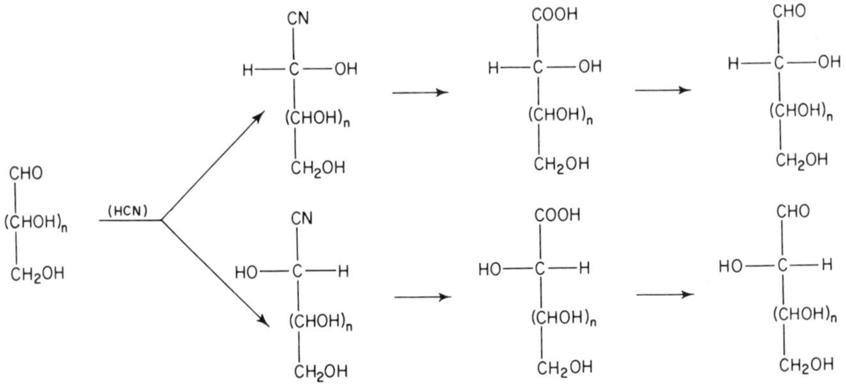

Below the structures of glycerose, and each of the tetroses and pentoses on page 60 have been drawn the two higher aldoses that are formed from each of them by the Kiliani synthesis. The assignment of configurations is founded on the fact that the structure designated as D-glycerose (1) was originally assumed to be, and has since been proved to be, the compound (+)-glycerose, (see p. 43). When this compound is converted to two tetroses by the Kiliani synthesis a mixture of (−)-erythrose and (+)-threose results. When each of these sugars is oxidised with nitric acid a dicarboxylic acid (a tartaric acid) is formed. That from (−)-erythrose is optically inactive and hence its molecules must be symmetrical; that from (+)-threose is optically active and its molecules must be dissymmetrical:

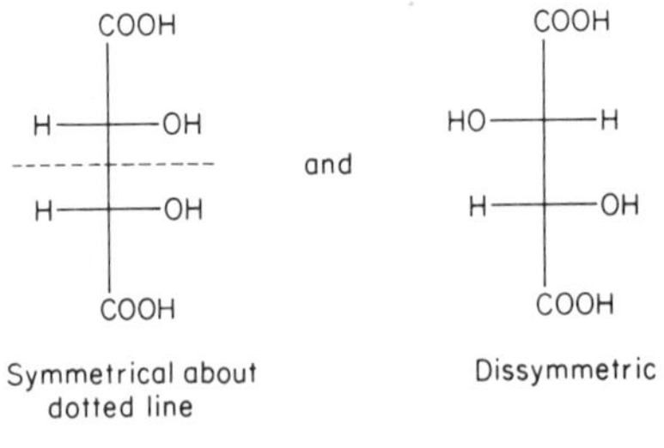

It follows that structures 2 and 3 must be (−)-erythrose and (+)-threose respectively.

It is found that the two aldopentoses formed from (−)-erythrose by the Kiliani synthesis are (−)-ribose and (−)-arabinose. On oxidation with nitric acid(−)-ribose gives an optically inactive dicarboxylic acid while (−)-arabinose gives an optically active one. They must therefore have structures 4 and 5 respectively. Again, the pentoses formed from (+)-threose are (+)-xylose, which gives an optically inactive dicarboxylic acid, and (−)-lyxose which gives an optically active one. Hence, their structures must be 6 and 7 respectively.

The aldohexoses formed from (−)-ribose are (+)-allose, which gives an optically inactive dicarboxylic acid, and hence has structure 8; and (+)-altrose which gives an active acid, and hence has structure 9. (−)-Lyxose yields (+)-galactose and (+)-talose which are assigned structures 14 and 15 for the same reasons.

(−)-Arabinose yields a mixture of (+)-glucose and (+)-mannose; hence, these sugars must have structures 10 and 11, or 11 and 10, respectively. It follows that (−)-gulose and (−)-idose which are formed from (+)-xylose, must have structures 12 and 13, or 13 and 12, respectively. The precise structures of these four sugars are assigned as follows. If they are oxidised with nitric acid, four different dicarboxylic acids are formed. But those formed from (+)-glucose and (−)-gulose are found to be enantiomers. Hence (+)-glucose and (−)-gulose must have structures 10 and 12 respectively, since only they will give mirror-image dicarboxylic acids, thus:

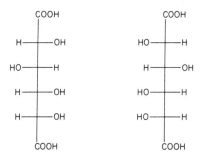

(The projection formula of the acid formed from (−)-gulose has been rotated through 180° (see p. 40) to make the mirror-image relationship clearer.) It follows that (+)-mannose and (−)-idose have structures 11 and 13 respectively.

Ketohexoses have three asymmetric carbons. The four predicted D-structures for those with the ketone group on C_2 are:

1.(+)-Psicose 2.(−)-Fructose 3.(+)-Sorbose 4.(+)-Tagatose

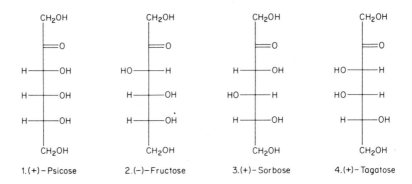

Four ketohexoses of this type are in fact known: psicose, fructose, sorbose and tagatose. (+)-Psicose gives the same osazone (see p. 72) as D-allose and hence has structure 1:

D–Allose Osazone (+)–Psicose

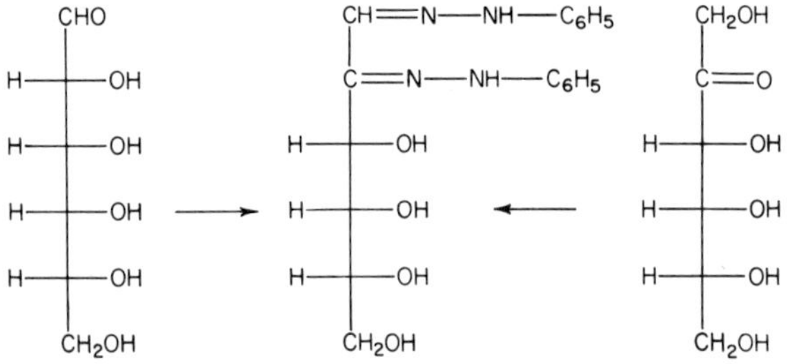

(−)-Fructose and D-glucose, (+)-sorbose and D-gulose, and (+)-tagatose and D-galactose give the same osazones. Hence (−)-fructose, (+)-sorbose and (+)-tagatose have structures 2, 3, and 4 respectively.

2. *Ring Structures of Monosaccharides*

The principal evidence that glucose molecules can exist as six-membered rings may be summarised as follows. The proof of the ring structure of other sugars is similar.

(1) Normal aldehydes react with two moles of methanol in the presence of hydrogen chloride to give compounds named acetals. But glucose reacts

with only one mole of methanol with the elimination of one mole of water, to give a mixture of two compounds (α- and β-methylglucosides) with the properties of acetals—notably stability to alkalis but lability to acids. This suggests that in most molecules the aldehyde group has already reacted with one hydroxyl within the same molecule, so forming a ring:

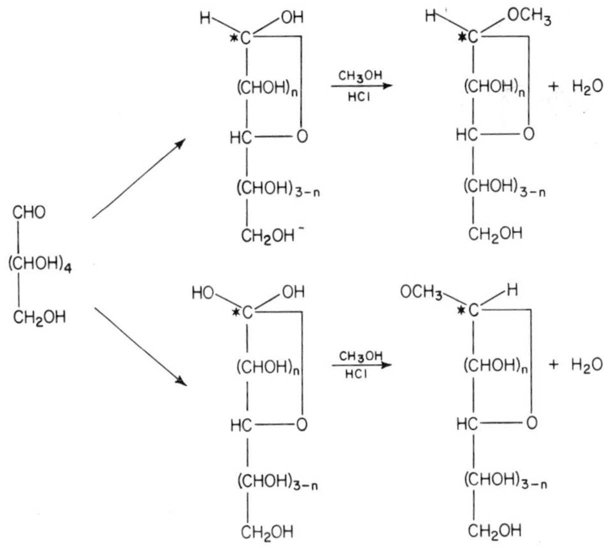

Since ring formation turns C_1 into an asymmetric carbon (shown asterisked) two methylglucosides which are diastereoisomers would in fact be expected. Also glucose does not colour Schiff's reagent like other aldehydes, suggesting that the aldehyde group is masked.

(2) If glucose molecules do form internal rings there should also be two forms of glucose which are diastereoisomers. Two forms of glucose can in fact be isolated. Ordinary crystalline glucose (α-glucose) gives solutions of specific rotation $+113°$. But glucose of specific rotation $+19°$ (β-glucose) can be prepared by crystallisation from a concentrated aqueous solution at $110°$. Over a few hours the specific rotations of solutions of both α- and β-glucose change to $+52°$. This is known as mutarotation, and is explained by an equilibrium mixture of α- and β-glucose being formed. When a solution of α-methyglucoside is hydrolysed by the enzyme maltase, α-glucose is formed as shown by a gradual fall in the optical rotation of the resulting solution. Similarly when β-methylglucoside is hydrolysed with the enzyme emulsin, β-glucose is formed, as shown by a gradual rise in rotation. (Since α- and β-glucose are diastereoisomers, and hence compounds with different properties, it

might be expected that they would each be given a new name other than glucose. This is not done because their properties are not readily distinguished since, in solution, they are interconverted and are also in equilibrium with open-chain glucose. The α- and β- forms of other sugars are also interconverted in solution as shown by mutarotation.)

(3) The above evidence can only be explained if glucose molecules exist predominantly as rings; and, because of strain, only five- or six-membered rings are likely. That the rings of α- and β-methylglucosides, which yield α- and β-glucose on hydrolysis are not five-membered is proved as follows. If α- or β-methylglucoside is methylated (see p. 72), and the methyl on C_1 then removed by acid hydrolysis, a tetramethylglucose is obtained. When this is oxidised with nitric acid, amongst the products is a trimethoxyglutaric acid. Since this contains three adjacent methoxy groups the original glucose must have had three adjacent hydroxyls which were not involved in ring formation. Only the six-membered ring has this:

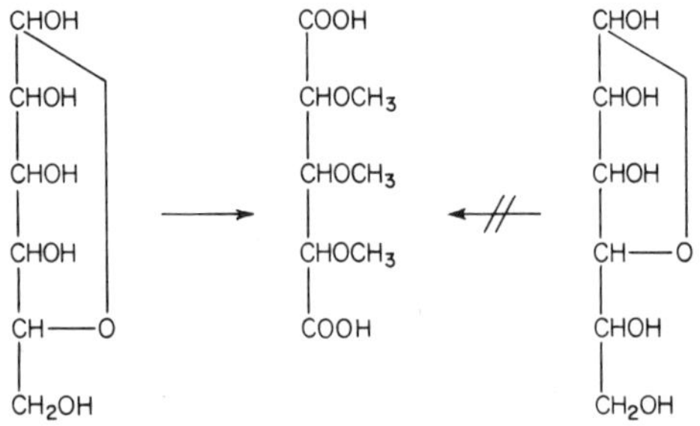

That the methylglucosides have six-membered rings is confirmed by periodate oxidation (see p. 71).

(4) X-ray diffraction measurements prove conclusively that all the molecules of crystalline glucose are six-membered rings.

When crystalline, all other pentoses and hexoses also exist as six-membered rings. In solution, five-membered rings exist in small concentration, as shown by the fact that a sugar may react to give a derivative with a five-membered ring. Thus glucose with methanol containing 1% hydrogen chloride at room temperature yields mainly α- and β-methylglucofuranosides, which methylation and degradation show to have five-membered rings:

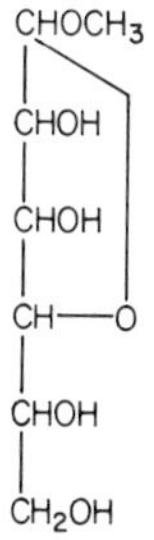

$$
\begin{array}{c}
\text{CHOCH}_3 \\
| \\
\text{CHOH} \\
| \\
\text{CHOH} \\
| \\
\text{CH}\!-\!\!-\text{O} \\
| \\
\text{CHOH} \\
| \\
\text{CH}_2\text{OH}
\end{array}
$$

Boiling methanol with 3% hydrogen chloride yields the normal α- and β-methylglucopyranosides. [Five-membered sugar rings are called furanose rings since, like furan the ring has four carbons and one oxygen. Six-membered sugar rings are called pyranose since they resemble pyran.]

Sugar rings are normally drawn in a way which corresponds more closely to their true structures as shown by molecular models. α-D-Glucopyranose and β-D-glucofuranose for example are drawn as:

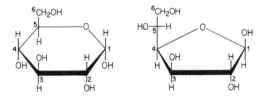

In these structures the plane of each ring is understood to lie perpendicular to the plane of the paper—as the plane of a coin would do if stood on its edge on the paper. The bonds which do not form the ring lie perpendicular to the plane of the ring. It was emphasised in the last chapter that free rotation can occur between all the carbon atoms of an open-chain sugar; and that if hydroxyls on adjacent carbons are shown as *cis* this is merely the result of the carbon atoms having been rotated until bonds to the hydrogen and hydroxyl groups rise out of the paper as required for Fischer projection formulae (see p. 40). However, in sugar rings free rotation between carbons is restricted, as it is in cyclohexane derivatives, and the hydroxyl groups are permanently *cis* or *trans* as shown (see p. 18).

It is seen above that in α-glucose the hydroxyl on C_1 lies *cis* to that on C_2, while in β-glucose it is *trans*. This is proved by the fact that α-glucose, in boric acid solution, has a higher electrical conductivity than β-glucose; it is known that cyclic glycols with *cis* hydroxyls raise the conductivity of boric acid due to the formation of complex ions. In all aldoses, if the hydroxyl on C_1 lies below the plane of the ring when orientated as above, the sugar is given the prefix α-; if above the plane of the ring, the prefix β-. Ketoses form rings by reaction of the ketone group on C_2 with another hydroxyl. If the resulting hydroxyl on C_2 lies below the plane of the ring the sugar is given the prefix α-; if above, the prefix β-. Thus α-D-fructo-pyranose and β-D-fructofuranose are:

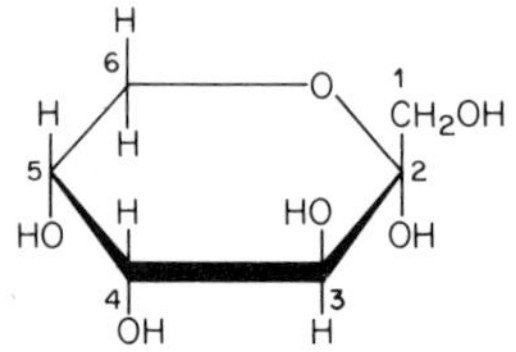

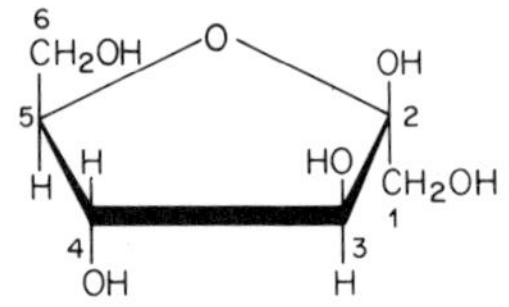

Molecular models show that when a hexose ring is closed on C_5, the CH_2OH group on C_5 lies above the plane of the ring in these formulae in a D-hexose and below it in an L-hexose. The formulae of β-L-glucopyranose and α-L-fructofuranose, which are the enantiomers of α-D-glucopyranose and β-D-fructofuranose shown above, illustrate this:

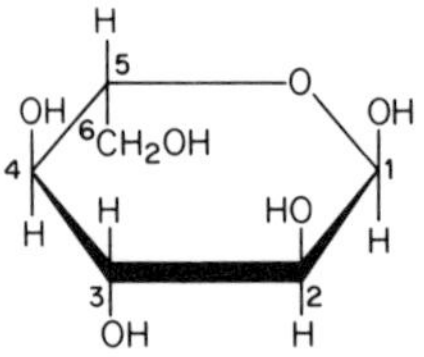

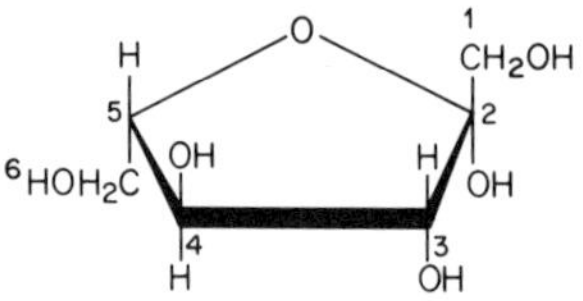

The above ring formulae are incorrect in showing the rings as planar, with hydroxyl groups at fixed distances apart. The rings are in fact buckled like those of cyclohexane, and usually exist in one of the two possible chair conformations (see p. 16). The distances between hydroxyls differ in the two chair conformations, and the sugar tends to assume the conformation in which repulsions between groups are minimal. Thus, in crystalline β-D-glucopyranose the molecules are all in that chair conformation in which all large groups are equatorial (a) rather than axial (b):

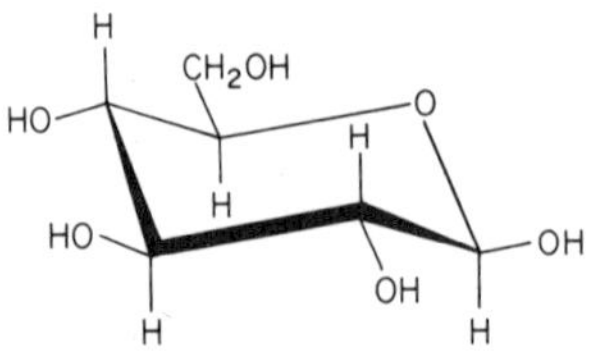

(a) 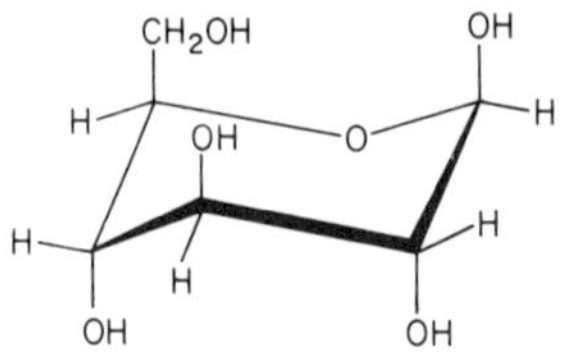   (b)

Knowledge of these facts allows certain chemical properties of sugars to be predicted, but is less important in biochemistry where the planar ring formulae are normally adequate.

The pyranose structures of some sugars other than D-glucose and D-fructose that occur free or combined in nature are shown below:

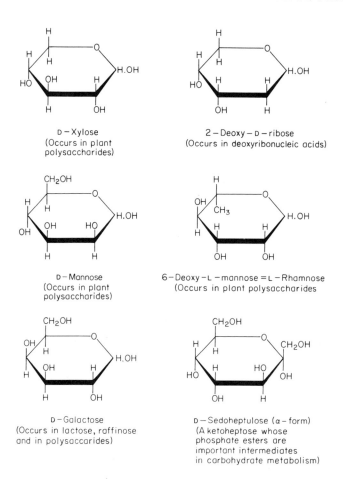

D—Xylose
(Occurs in plant polysaccharides)

2—Deoxy—D—ribose
(Occurs in deoxyribonucleic acids)

D—Mannose
(Occurs in plant polysaccharides)

6—Deoxy—L—mannose = L—Rhamnose
(Occurs in plant polysaccharides

D—Galactose
(Occurs in lactose, raffinose and in polysaccarides)

D—Sedoheptulose (α—form)
(A ketoheptose whose phosphate esters are important intermediates in carbohydrate metabolism)

More sugars that occur in nature are D- than L-; that is, their penultimate carbons have the D- configuration. This fact is often thought to have biological significance, as in the following quotation: "Virtually all natural amino acids are L-, all natural sugars D- . . .". The fact that all protein amino acids have the same configuration on the α-carbon has biological significance: right-handed helixes in proteins are founded on it (see p. 117). Hence an organism that incorporated a D-amino acid into its

proteins would presumably not survive. It is however difficult to see any
survival value to an organism in having the penultimate carbon of most of
its sugars of one configuration. It has probably happened by chance—and
it has been brought to our attention because we happen to have chosen the
configuration of this carbon for classifying sugars as D- or L-.

3. Properties of Monosaccharides

Monosaccharides are colourless crystalline compounds which decompose
on heating, without precise melting points. They taste sweet. Aldoses and
ketoses do not affect Schiff's reagent but both reduce Fehling's solution
and ammoniacal silver nitrate. These properties are due to the ready
oxidation of the carbonyl carbon which is known as the "reducing carbon".
The other principal properties of aldoses and ketoses are summarised
below:

(1) Aldoses are readily oxidised and, without loss of carbon atoms,
can give molecules of three types. If the aldehyde group alone is oxidised
to carboxyl the product is known as an "-onic" acid. Thus glucose with
bromine water yields gluconic acid which forms a γ-lactone:

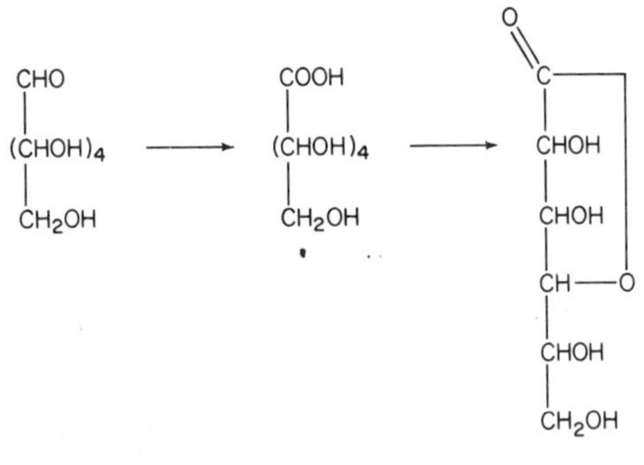

More vigorous oxidation converts both terminal groups to carboxyl,
yielding the "-aric" acid. Thus glucose with nitric acid gives glucaric acid
(also known as saccharic acid):

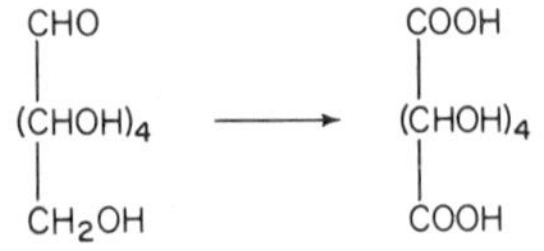

A third type of oxidation product, a "-uronic" acid results from the
oxidation of the terminal CH_2OH group only to carboxyl. This oxidation

cannot be done directly. Glucuronic acid, for example, is obtained by reducing the lactone of glucaric acid.

Ketoses are less readily oxidised than aldoses and are severed to give products with less carbon atoms. Thus fructose gives D-erythronic acid $CH_2OH(CHOH)_2COOH$, and glycollic acid $CH_2OHCOOH$.

(2) Periodate will oxidise compounds with a series of two or more primary or secondary hydroxyl groups on adjacent carbon atoms, and carbohydrates are such compounds. The reaction is well illustrated by the oxidation of glucose:

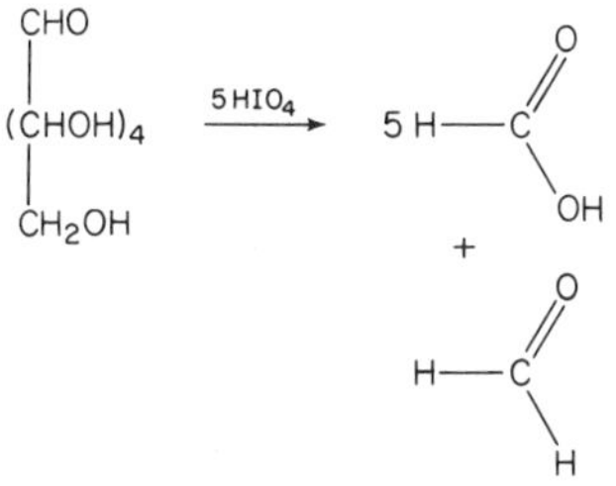

C_6 gives a molecule of formaldehyde since it carries a primary alcoholic group; the carbons which carry secondary alcoholic groups, and the aldehyde group of C_1, each give a molecule of formic acid. Each carbon—carbon bond that is severed requires one mole of periodate.

This reaction is very useful for determining carbohydrate structures, largely because it occurs quantitatively. The periodate used can be determined by back titration with potassium iodide. The formic acid produced can be determined by titration, and the formaldehyde by its reaction with dimedone. The following is an example of its usefulness. Methyl α-D-glucopyranoside requires two moles of periodate for its oxidation and gives one mole of formic acid. Methyl α-D-arabinofuranoside requires one mole of periodate and gives no formic acid. These facts prove that the two compounds have six- and five-membered rings respectively; and since they both yield the same product it is also proved that they both have the same configuration on C_1, and on the penultimate carbon. These conclusions are made clear by the following formulae:

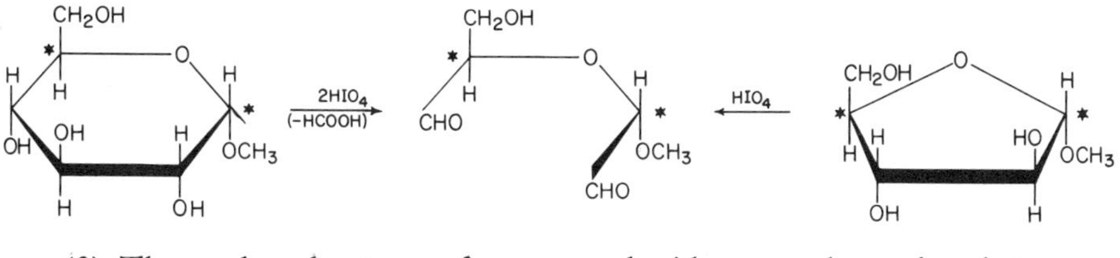

(3) The carbonyl group of monosaccharides may be reduced to hydroxyl with sodium amalgam or, better, sodium borohydride. Glucose, for example, yields sorbitol:

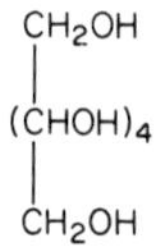

$$CH_2OH$$
$$|$$
$$(CHOH)_4$$
$$|$$
$$CH_2OH$$

(4) Like aldehyde and ketones, aldoses and ketoses will react with one mole of phenylhydrazine to form phenylhydrazones. But with excess phenylhydrazine a hydroxyl adjacent to the carbonyl is oxidised to carbonyl. This also reacts with phenylhydrazine and the product is an osazone. Osazones were invaluable to Fischer and others for isolating and identifying sugars, since each has a characteristic crystalline form. Their melting points, however, are not sharp. It has more recently been discovered that crystalline osatriazoles, with sharp melting points, are formed when osazones are heated with copper sulphate solution, and these can be more useful for identifying sugars. The following shows the formation of glucosazone and glucosatriazole from glucose, mannose, and fructose: (see facing page).

(5) The alcoholic hydroxyls of sugars can be converted to ether groups. Thus, if glucose is treated with methyl iodide and silver oxide or, better, with dimethyl sulphate and sodium hydroxide, pentamethyl glucose is formed:

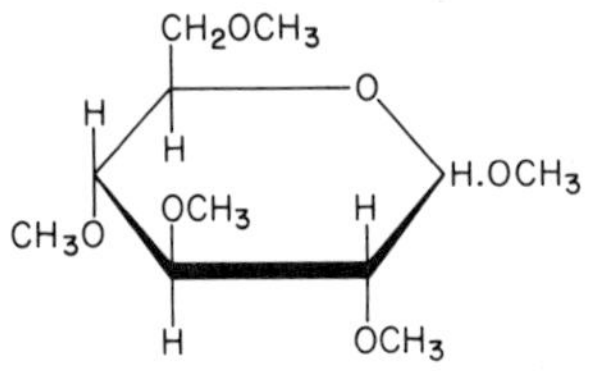

The methyl on C_1, being part of an acetal group, is removed by mild acid hydrolysis leaving the remaining stable ether groups.

(6) The hydroxyl groups can also be esterified. Thus, when glucose is heated with sodium acetate and acetic anhydride a penta-acetate is formed:

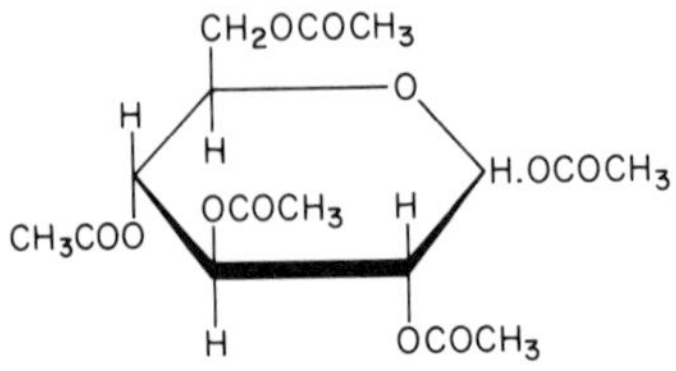

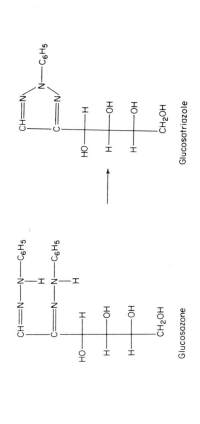

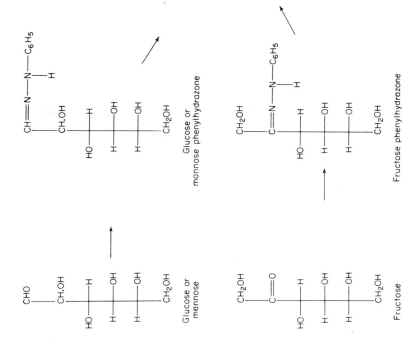

Esters of sugars with phosphoric acid, such as glucose 6-phosphate, are important in living organisms.

(7) It has been seen that sugars largely exist as rings formed by the carbonyl group reacting with a hydroxyl in the same molecule to form a hemiacetal. On ring formation a hydroxyl is formed on the carbon of the carbonyl group, which now exists in two mirror-image forms (α- and β-) since it has become an asymmetric carbon. This hydroxyl can react with the hydroxyl of another molecule, with the elimination of water, to form a diacetal. Such compounds in general are called α- and β-glycosides; individual glycosides are named after the sugar: glucosides, mannosides, fructosides, etc. The reaction of glucose with methanol to form α- and β-methylglucosides was described earlier (p. 64). Many glycosides of unknown function occur in plants. An example is arbutin in which hydroquinone is linked to glucose by a β-link:

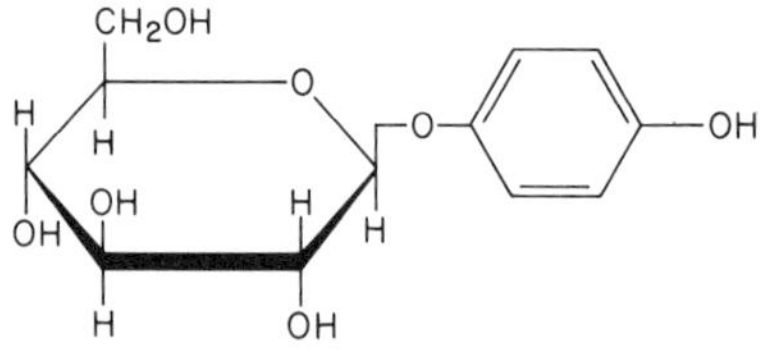

When a glycosidic link is formed with the hydroxyl of another sugar the product is a disaccharide.

Related compounds called glycosylamines, or nitrogen glycosides, are formed when the sugar reacts with an $=NH$ rather than an -OH group in another compound. They also exist in α- and β-forms. An example is adenosine in which water has been eliminated between the hydroxyl on C_1 of β-D-ribofuranose and the 9-imino group of adenine:

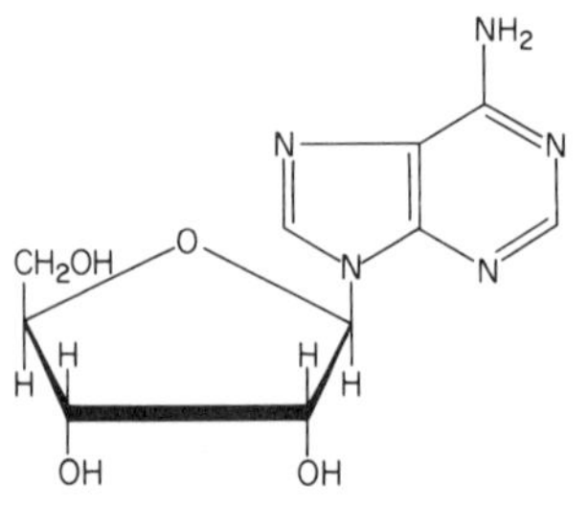

(8) Pentoses may be distinguished from hexoses by heating with dilute hydrochloric acid when they form furfural:

Furfural forms sparingly soluble derivatives with phloroglucinol and these may be used for the quantitative estimation of pentoses. Aldoses turn a special Schiff's reagent pink, which distinguishes them from ketoses.

4. Di-, Tri-, and Tetrasaccharides

Oligosaccharides are sometimes defined as sugars that contain from two to ten monosaccharide units. Of these, only di-, tri-, and tetra-saccharides occur naturally to any extent. They are all crystalline, sweet, soluble in water, and readily hydrolysed by dilute acids.

Disaccharides are of two kinds: reducing and nonreducing. In a reducing disaccharide the reducing carbon of one monosaccharide is linked glycosidically to a carbon, other than the reducing carbon, of another monosaccharide. In a nonreducing disaccharide the reducing carbon of one monosaccharide is linked glycosidically to the reducing carbon of another, so masking the reducing properties of both.

Only two disaccharides occur abundantly in nature: lactose from milk and sucrose (cane sugar or table sugar) from sugar beet and sugar cane. Their structures, and those of other important disaccharides are shown below: (see following page).

The methods by which the structures of disaccharides are established will be illustrated by the proofs of the structures of lactose and sucrose. The structure of lactose is proved as follows.

(1) On acid hydrolysis it gives one molecule of D-glucose and one of D-galactose. Its molecular weight shows it to be a disaccharide.

(2) It reduces Fehling's solution and forms an osazone. Hence at least one of the monosaccharide residues has a free reducing group.

(3) On oxidation with bromine water it gives lactobionic acid which, on hydrolysis, gives one molecule of galactose and one of gluconic acid. Hence C_1 of the glucose residue of lactose must be free, and C_1 of the galactose must be glycosidically linked to the glucose.

(4) It is hydrolysed by the enzyme emulsin (specific for β-glycosidic links) and not by maltase (specific for α-links). Hence galactose is linked to glucose by a β-glycosidic link.

(5) That the galactose ring is pyranose is proved as follows. Methylation of lactose gives octamethyl-lactose which, on hydrolysis gives one

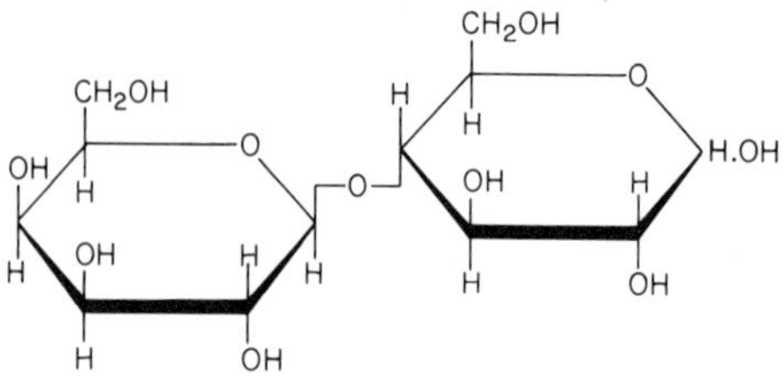

LACTOSE
4−(β−D−galactopyranosyl)−
D−glucopyranose

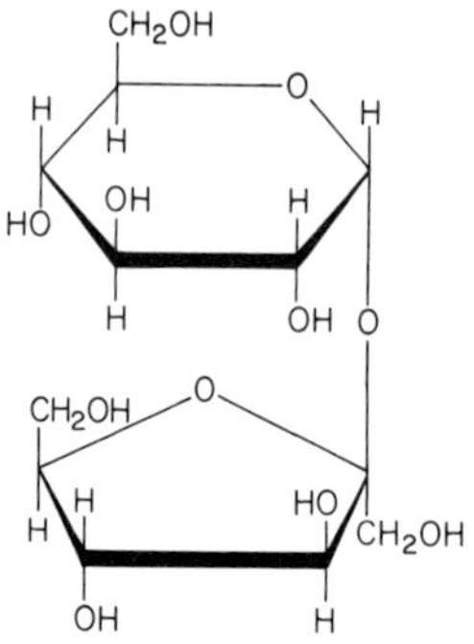

SUCROSE
α−D−glucopyranosyl−
β−D−fructofuranoside

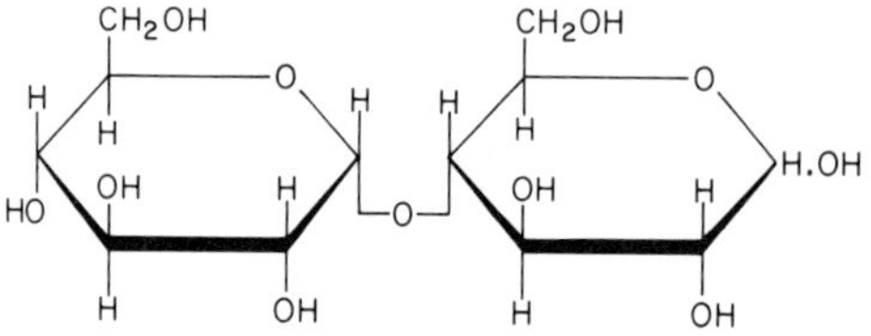

MALTOSE
(formed during hydrolysis of starch)
4−(α−D−glucopyranosyl)−
D−glucopyranose

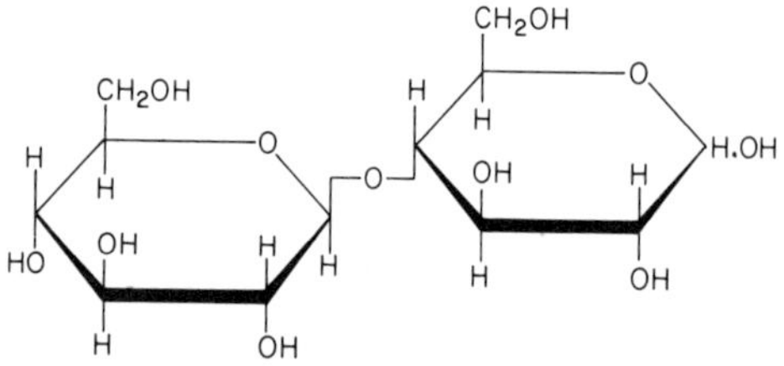

CELLOBIOSE
(formed during hydrolysis of cellulose)
4−(β−D−glucopyranosyl)−
D−glucopyranose

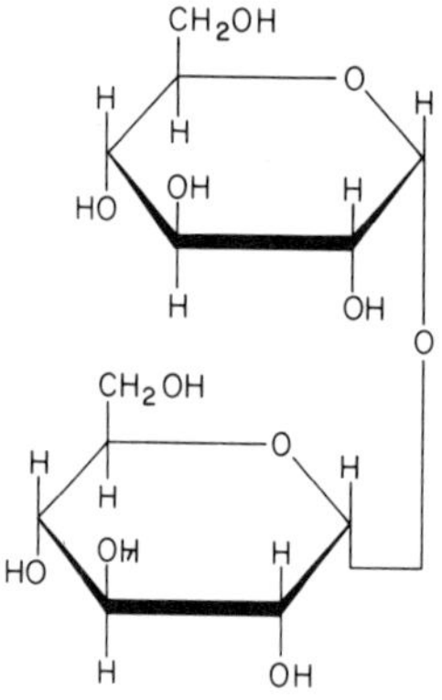

TREHALOSE
(occurs in yeasts and fungi)
α−D−glucopyranosyl−
α−D−glucopyranoside

molecule of methanol, one of 2,3,4,6-tetramethylgalactose, and one of 2,3,6-trimethylglucose:

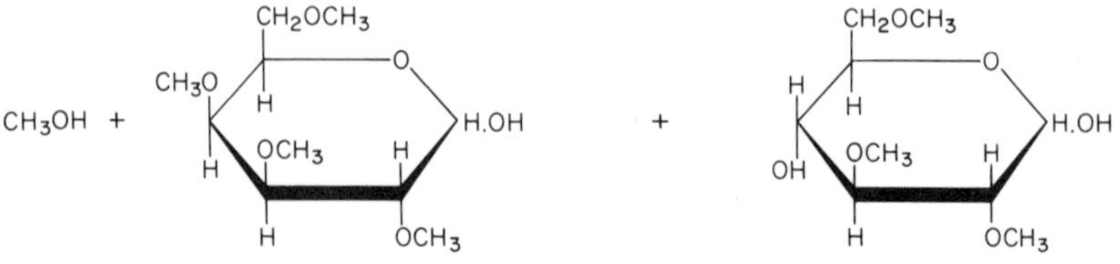

The methanol must have been glycosidically linked to C_1 of the glucose residue. The hydroxyls in the galactose and glucose that are methylated must be those that are free in lactose. It is clear that the galactose residue of lactose must be pyranose since only C_1 and C_5 are unmethylated. Also, since C_4 and C_5 of the glucose are unmethylated it is probable that, in lactose, C_5 is involved in a pyranose ring and C_4 is linked to C_1 of galactose. But it is possible that C_5 is linked to galactose while C_4 is in a furanose ring that rearranges to pyranose during the hydrolysis.

(6) That the glucose ring in lactose is in fact pyranose is proved as follows. Lactose is oxidised to lactobionic acid in which the glucose ring is opened, and the hydroxyl which was involved in ring formation is free to be methylated. On methylation and hydrolysis lactobionic acid yields 2,3,4,6-tetramethylgalactose as before, and 2,3,5,6-tetramethylgluconic acid. Since C_5 of the glucose residue has now been methylated this must have formed part of a pyranose ring, and C_4 must have been linked to C_1 of galactose. The structure of lactose is thus proved to be that shown previously (p. 76), these reactions being:

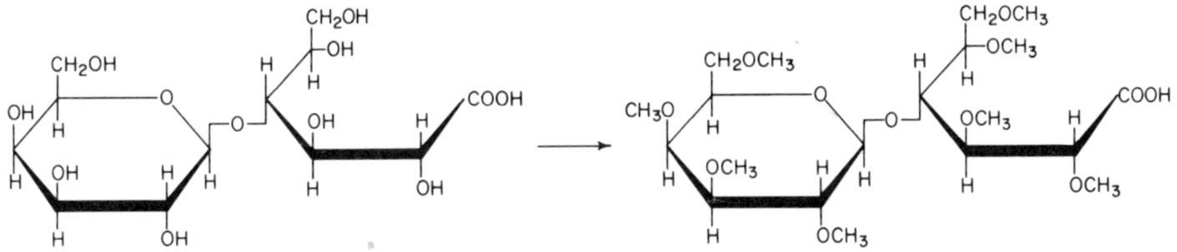

Lactobionic acid

Octamethyl — lactobionic acid

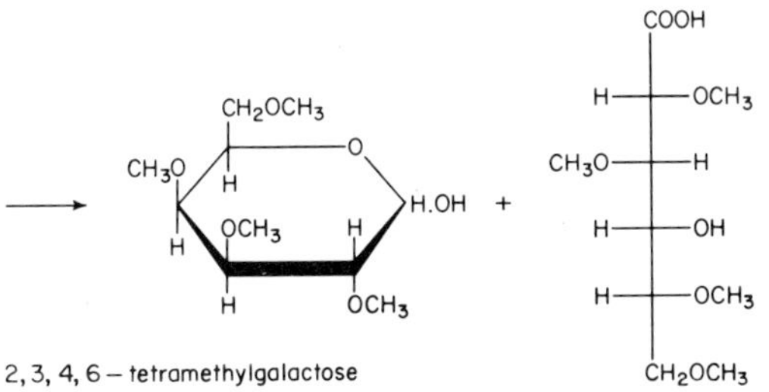

2, 3, 4, 6 — tetramethylgalactose

2, 3, 5, 6 — tetramethylgluconic acid

The structure of sucrose is proved as follows.

(1) On acid hydrolysis it gives one molecule of D-glucose and one of D-fructose. Its molecular weight shows it to be a disaccharide.

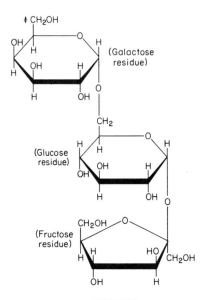

RAFFINOSE
(Occurs in plants. Note
glucose and fructose
linked as in sucrose)

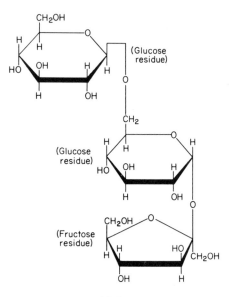

GENTIANOSE
(Occurs in gentian roots. Note
glucose and fructose linked
as in sucrose)

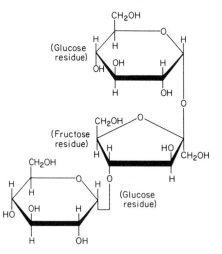

MELEZITOSE
(Occurs in honeydew of
lime trees. Note glucose
and fructose linked as in
sucrose)

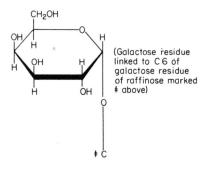

STACHYOSE
(A tetrasaccharide found
in plants)

(2) It does not reduce Fehling's solution nor does it react with phenyl-hydrazine. Hence the reducing carbon of glucose (C_1) must be linked to the reducing carbon of fructose (C_2).

(3) It is hydrolysed by maltase which is specific for α-glucosides. The specificities of other enzymes that will, and will not, hydrolyse sucrose prove that the linkage on C_1 of glucose is α, and on C_2 of fructose is β.

(4) The size of each ring is proved by methylation and hydrolysis: octamethylsucrose yields one molecule each of 2,3,4,6-tetramethylgluco-pyranose and 1,3,4,6-tetramethylfructofuranose. Hence the structure of sucrose is that shown previously (p. 76).

Three trisaccharides and one tetrasaccharide that occur in nature are shown on the facing page.

The ways in which the structures of tri- and tetrasaccharides are deduced are illustrated by the following proof of the structure of raffinose.

(1) On acid hydrolysis it gives one molecule each of D-glucose, D-galactose, and D-fructose. Its molecular weight shows it to be a tri-saccharide.

(2) Invertase, an enzyme that hydrolyses sucrose, yields D-fructose and the disaccharide melibiose which has been proved to be 6-(α-D-galactopyranosyl)-D-glucopyranose. The enzyme α-galactosidase yields sucrose and D-galactose.

5. Cellulose

Cellulose is a polysaccharide. Polysaccharide molecules are straight or branched chains of monosaccharide residues linked glycosidically. A polysaccharide can never be isolated chemically pure; at best it is a collec-tion of molecules of closely related molecular size and structure, since polysaccharides are synthesised in that way in animals and plants. Poly-saccharides serve two main functions. They may, like cellulose in plants and chitin in arthropods, form part of the inert structure of the organism. Or they may, like starch in certain plants and glycogen in mammals, act as a food reserve. The shape of the molecules is in accord with their function: structural polysaccharides tend to have long unbranched molecules which pack together as insoluble fibres; those that are food reserves tend to have more soluble branched molecules which come out of solution as granules.

Cellulose is the main component of the cell walls of plants. Cotton is 98% cellulose while wood and straw contain around 50%. Pure cellulose is isolated from cotton, or other plant materials, by heating with dilute sodium hydroxide, in the absence of air, to remove pectin (see p. 89), waxes, and oils. Traces of coloured impurities are then removed by treating with dilute sodium hypochlorite. Cellulose is insoluble in water and most other solvents. Its structure has been proved as follows.

(1) Elementary analysis shows its empirical formula to be $C_6H_{10}O_5$. Its molecular weight is very high.

(2) Hydrolysis by concentrated acids at low temperatures can give almost theoretical yields of D-glucose.

(3) On acetylation with a mixture of acetic acid, acetic anhydride, and sulphuric acid, three acetyl radicals are added per residue of glucose, suggesting that each residue has three free hydroxyls.

(4) On treatment of celluose, under the correct conditions, with a mixture of acetic anhydride and sulphuric acid about 50% is converted to the acetate of cellobiose (see p. 72). Under the same conditions glucose does not form cellobiose, and hence cellulose must contain cellobiose units. Higher oligosaccharides with glucose residues also joined by β-1,4-links can be isolated after mild acid hydrolysis of cellulose. No oligosaccharides with α-links have been obtained, and cellulose is stable to enzymes that hydrolyse them.

(5) Complete methylation of cellulose, with dimethyl sulphate in an inert atmosphere, followed by acid hydrolysis gives a high yield of 2,3,6-trimethylglucose, plus about 0.5 to 1% of 2,3,4,6-tetramethylglucose.

It may be concluded that cellulose is composed of long molecules in which D-glucose residues are joined by β-1,4-links:

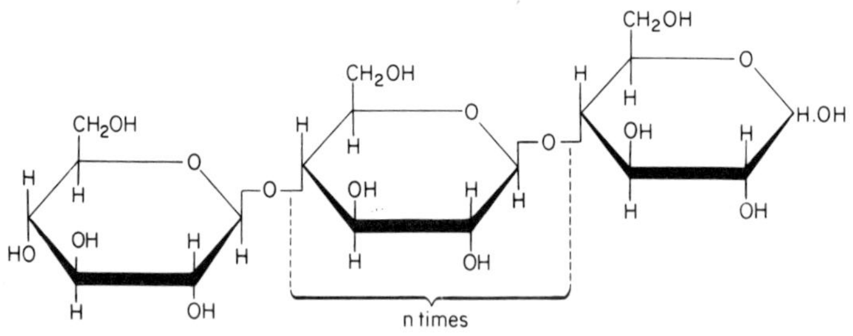

The 2,3,4,6-tetramethylglucose obtained on hydrolysis of methylated cellulose must come from residues at the nonreducing ends of the chains, and its yield suggests that the chains have 100 to 200 residues. However the chains apparently break during methylation, since ultracentrifuge and viscosity measurements suggest that undegraded cellulose molecules can have 2000 to 3000 glucose residues, the number varying from one molecule to the next. The chain length appears to vary from one kind of plant to another, although differences may arise from breakage during isolation.

X-ray diffraction measurements show that the molecules in a cellulose fibre are aligned along the fibre axis. The fibres have a repeating characteristic at every 10.3 Å along their length, rather than about every 5.1 Å which is the length of a glucose residue. This is explained by alternate glucose residues being rotated through 180° from the structure shown above:

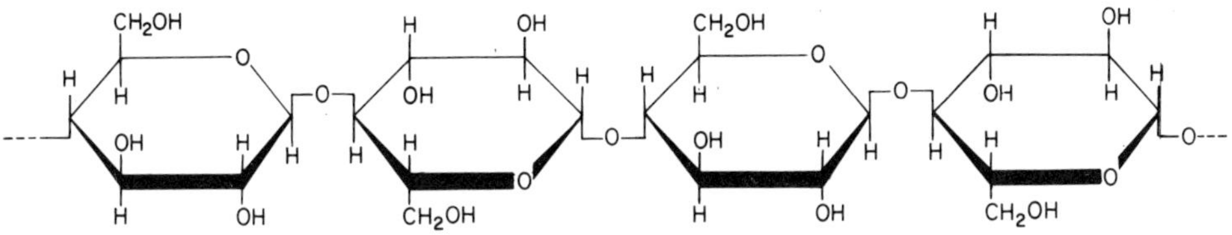

The molecules appear to be bound together by hydrogen bonds between the hydroxyls of adjacent glucose residues. The structure on which a cotton thread depends for its strength can therefore be traced down to its component molecules: the thread is made from cotton fibres twisted together lengthways, while the cotton fibres are themselves made from cellulose molecules packed together lengthways. The tensile strength of cellulose fibres is also important in maintaining the structure of plant cells.

6. Starch and Glycogen

Starch is a food reserve of plants, being a reserve of glucose residues with negligible osmotic pressure. It is easily degraded during isolation. The least degraded starch is isolated from potatoes by extraction with boiling water under nitrogen, followed by a brief treatment with sodium hypochlorite.

Starch forms viscous solutions in water with low osmotic pressures. Physical measurements give molecular weights of 10^6 to 10^8. Starch contains two components, amylose and amylopectin, that can be separated by selective precipitation. In one method n-butanol is added to a hot aqueous solution of starch when amylose separates as needles on cooling. Amylopectin is then precipitated from the mother liquor by adding methanol. Corn starch, and most other starches, contain about 25% amylose and 75% amylopectin. But starches in certain peas are almost pure amylose, while others in certain cereals are almost pure amylopectin. Amylose is soluble in hot water but separates as crystals on cooling; amylopectin is soluble in hot and cold water and does not separate on cooling. Amylose gives a pure blue with iodine; amylopectin gives a less intense violet.

The structure of amylose has been proved as follows:

(1) Its molecular weight is very high. On acid hydrolysis it gives a quantitative yield of D-glucose.

(2) With amylase enzymes, which hydrolyse α-glycosidic links, it gives an almost quantitative yield of maltose (see p. 76).

(3) On methylation and hydrolysis it gives 2,3,6-trimethylglucose and 2,3,4,6-tetramethylglucose in a molar ratio of 200-300:1.

It may be concluded that amylose molecules are primarily long chains of D-glucose residues joined by α-1,4-links:

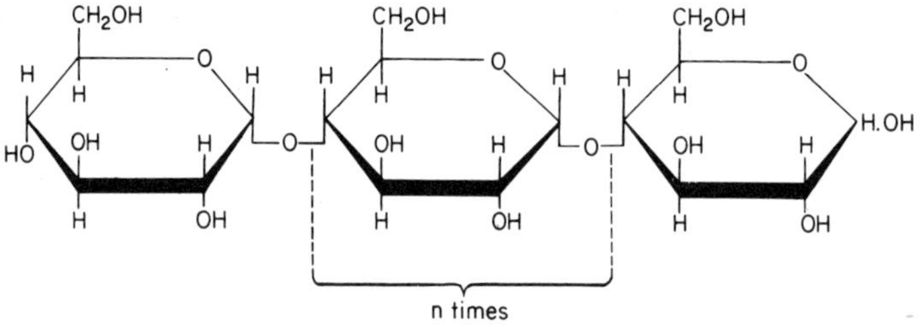

However, hydrolysis by purified amylases is not always complete, suggesting that glucose residues may occasionally be joined by other than α-1,4-links.

The relative yields of the two methylated glucoses suggest that the molecules have 200 to 300 glucose residues. But physical molecular weight determinations suggest there are 1000 to 4000 residues, the number varying from one molecule to the next. It is therefore clear that amylose is degraded during methylation. X-ray diffraction shows that amylose molecules are long helixes with about six glucose residues to each turn.

The structure of amylopectin is proved as follows.

(1) Its molecular weight is very high. On acid hydrolysis it gives a quantitative yield of D-glucose.

(2) It can be completely hydrolysed to glucose only by the combined action of enzymes specific for α-1,4- and α-1,6-glucosidic links.

(3) On methylation and hydrolysis it yields 2,3,6-trimethylglucose, 2,3,4,6-tetramethylglucose, and 2,3-dimethylglucose in molar ratios of about 20:1:1.

(4) After mild acid hydrolysis isomaltose, in which two glucose residues are joined by α-1,6-links, can be isolated.

(5) It is concluded from this evidence that the large amylopectin molecules are built up from short chains of α-1,4-linked glucose residues (usually twenty to twenty-five); these chains are joined by α-1,6-links:

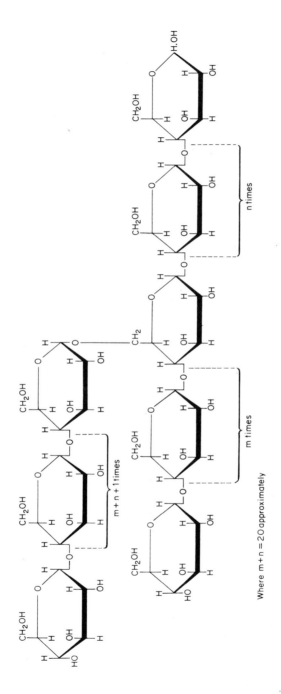

Where m + n = 20 approximately

83

It is as though thousands of snakes (chains of twenty to twenty-five glucose residues) formed a large structure by every snake but one embedding its teeth (C_1 of the terminal residue) somewhere along the back of another. Three distinct structures of this type are possible:

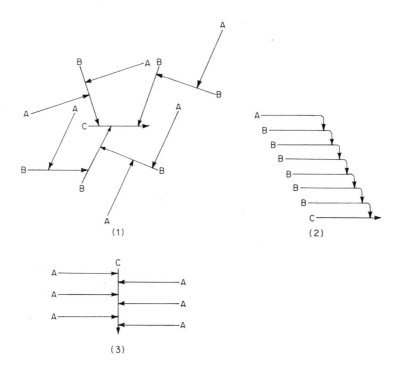

(1)   (2)

(3)

(The head of each arrow represents the reducing carbon of a short chain.) It is convenient to distinguish in these structures chains of three types: *A*-chains which are joined to only one other chain through C_1 of the terminal residue (i.e., snakes that bite but are not bitten); *B*-chains which are joined to another chain in this way, and also to one or more additional chains by links from C_6 of certain of their residues (i.e., snakes which both bite, and are bitten one or more times); and *C*-chains which have a terminal residue with C_1 free (i.e., snakes which are bitten but do not bite). Each of the above structures has only one *C*-chain, but the ratio of *A*- to *B*-chains differs. In structure 1 there are roughly equal numbers of *A*- and *B*-chains; in structure 2 there is only one *A*-chain; while in structure 3 there are no *B* chains.

That amylopectin has structure 1 has been proved by the successive action of two enzymes from higher plants: *β*-amylase which is specific for residues at the nonreducing terminus of *α*-1,4-linked glucose chains, and

"R-enzyme" which is specific for α-1,6-glucosidic links. On digestion with β-amylase about 55% of the glucose residues of amylopectin are removed leaving a "β-limit dextrin". If this is hydrolysed by the R-enzyme a mixture of straight oligosaccharides is formed which either have two or three glucose residues (i.e., maltose and maltotriose) or many more. It is concluded that when β-amylase acts on amylopectin it removes successive glucose residues from the chain ends but is inhibited as it approaches the α-1,6-branches. When the limit dextrin is hydrolysed, maltose and maltotriose come from the stubs of the A-chains while the larger oligosaccharides come from the B-chains. It is found that roughly 13% of the glucose residues of the limit dextrin are obtained as maltose and maltotriose (from the A-chains) and the remainder as oligosaccharides of average chain length about twenty-one (from B-chains). This will be the result only if amylopectin contains roughly equal numbers of A- and B- chains and hence it must have a structure of type 1. Experiments with other enzymes confirm this. Since amylopectin molecules contain around one million glucose residues it is clear that in a sample of amylopectin few molecules will have identical structures; they can differ from one another in their total number of glucose residues, in the lengths of the thousands of subsidiary chains, and in the position along one chain that another is attached.

Glycogen is a carbohydrate reserve of animals. In mammals it occurs mainly in liver and muscles. It is isolated by extracting the starting material with hot potassium hydroxide followed by precipitation of glycogen with ethanol. Its molecular weight is around one million, and on acid hydrolysis it gives only glucose. Similar evidence proves that it has a similar structure to amylopectin, except that the component chains are shorter, having ten to fourteen glucose residues.

7. Other Polysaccharides

Polysaccharides occur in the whole range of living organisms from bacteria and protozoa to man. There are innumerable variations in structure, which are illustrated below by the more important polysaccharides.

A. Other glucans

Cellulose and starch are glucans—polysaccharides composed solely, or almost solely, of glucose. Glucans of other structures also occur. One is laminarin, extracted from the seaweed *Laminaria* with dilute acid. Its structure is proved as follows:

(1) Its molecular weight is around 4000. On hydrolysis it gives D-glucose in 99% yield.

(2) On methylation and hydrolysis 2,4,6-trimethylglucose and 2,3,4,6-tetramethylglucose are formed in a molar ratio of about 20:1.

(3) The direction of its optical rotation is characteristic of polysaccharides with β-linked residues.

(4) After mild acid hydrolysis the disaccharide laminaribiose can be isolated. It has two glucose residues joined by β-1,3-links.

(5) It is concluded that laminarin molecules are basically straight chains of about twenty β-1,3-linked glucose residues:

However, after partial hydrolysis it is possible to isolate small amounts of gentiobiose consisting of two β-1,6-linked glucose residues. This suggests that some glucose residues in straight chains are β-1,6-linked or that two chains may sometimes be joined by β-1,6-branches. Moreover, the reducing ability of laminarin is less than expected if one glucose residue in twenty had its reducing group free; also, after partial hydrolysis, oligosaccharides can be isolated with a terminal mannitol (see p. 71) residue linked from C_1 or C_6 to C_1 of a glucose residue. It is concluded that some of the chains of laminarin terminate not with glucose, but with mannitol linked to glucose in this way.

Glucans also occur in yeast and appear to consist of straight chains of β-1,3- and β-1,6-linked glucose residues. Lichenin from certain lichens is a glucan, and consists of chains of around one hundred glucose residues about 70% of which are β-1,4-linked and 30% β-1,3-linked, the two kinds of link occurring at random along the chains.

Leuconostoc bacteria, when grown on sucrose form glucans named dextrans. Their molecular weights are about ten million and they are built up from chains of about twenty α-1,6-linked glucose residues. These form structures resembling amylopectin by α-1,2-, α-1,3- and α-1,4-branches. These dextrans, after partial hydrolysis to a molecular weight of about 60,000, are added to saline for blood transfusion. Like plasma proteins they do not permeate the capillary walls and hence maintain a higher osmotic pressure within the vessels than without, so preventing edema.

B. Fructans

Inulin is the most important fructan—polysaccharides that yield almost only fructose on hydrolysis. This, rather than starch, is the carbohydrate reserve in the roots of *Compositae*. It may be extracted from the tubers of dandelions, dahlias, or artichokes with hot water, from which it separates after concentrating and cooling. Its structure is proved as follows:

(1) Its molecular weight is around 5000. On acid hydrolysis it yields only fructose and a trace of glucose.

(2) Methylation and hydrolysis yields 3,4,6-trimethylfructofuranose and 1,3,4,6-tetramethylfructofuranose in a molar ratio of about 30:1, plus a trace of methylated glucose.

(3) The optical rotation of inulin solutions shows that its residues are β-linked, and it is concluded that inulin molecules are basically straight chains of about thirty β-1,2-linked fructofuranose residues.

(4) However, inulin has little reducing ability, suggesting that the chains do not terminate in a fructose residue with its reducing carbon free. Moreover, sucrose can be isolated after partial hydrolysis of inulin. It is concluded that the reducing carbon of the terminal fructose residue of each chain is linked to C_1 of a glucose residue as in sucrose. In fact inulin appears to be formed in plants by successively adding fructose residues to a sucrose molecule. The structure of inulin is therefore:

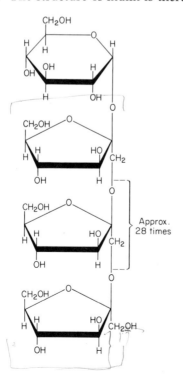

Other fructans occur in the leaves of many grasses and are called levans. Their molecules are straight chains of around twenty β-2,6-linked fructose residues, again terminating in a residue of sucrose. Similar levans occur in bacteria, but the molecules are larger and, in some, the chains branch from C_1 of certain fructose residues. Branched levans have also been found in plants.

C. Xylans

Hemicelluloses are a group of polysaccharides associated with cellulose in the cell walls of plants, and their most important components are xylans. All these xylans give:

(1) On complete hydrolysis, D-xylopyranose in high yields.
(2) On partial hydrolysis, xylobiose, xylotriose, and higher oligo-saccharides all composed of β-1,4-linked xylopyranose residues.
(3) On methylation and hydrolysis, 2,3-dimethylxylose.

The optical rotation of solutions of xylans shows that the residues are β-linked. It is concluded that all xylans are basically chains of β-1,4-linked xylopyranose residues:

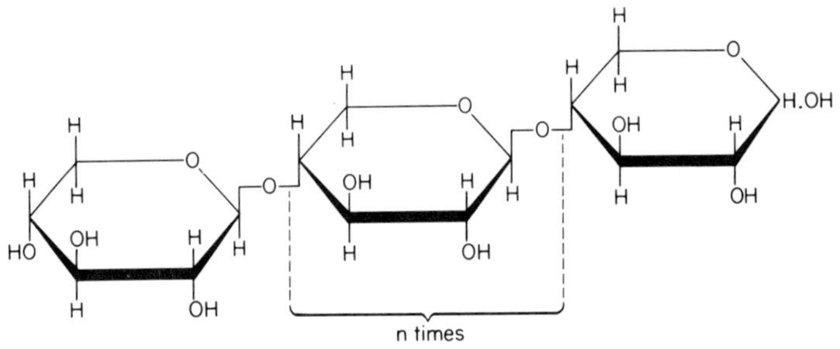

Asparto grass xylan has mainly this structure with about fifty residues per chain, although occasional branching from C_3 of certain xylose residues does seem to occur.

Some other xylans give small yields of other sugars on hydrolysis. Wheat straw xylan gives L-arabinose, and the manner in which this is linked is suggested by the following facts:

(1) On methylation of the xylan and hydrolysis small amounts of 2,3,5-trimethylarabinose can be isolated.
(2) L-Arabinose can be removed by mild hydrolysis that does not sever the xylose chains.

(3) A trisaccharide has been isolated from enzymic hydrolysates with the structure:

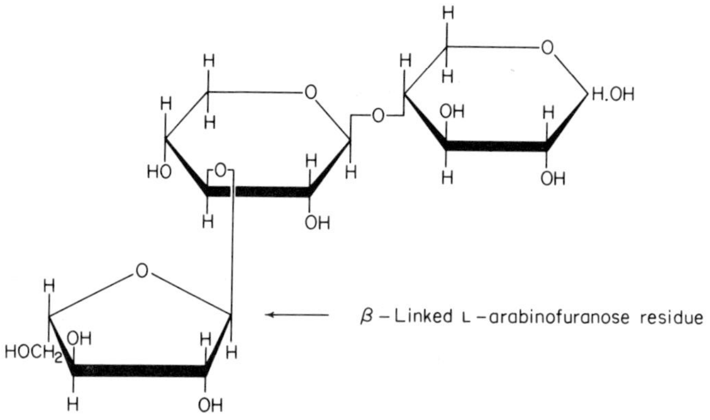

β – Linked L –arabinofuranose residue

It is concluded that L-arabinofuranose residues are attached at intervals along the chains of xylose residues as single β-1,3-linked branches.

Some xylans, such as beechwood xylan, yield small amounts of D-glucuronic acid or 4-methylglucuronic acid on hydrolysis. These are linked in the same way as the arabinose residues of wheat straw xylan.

D. Mannans

Hemicelluloses also contain mannans which are largely composed of β-1,4-linked D-mannopyranose residues. Glucomannans occur in coniferous woods and contain D-glucopyranose and D-mannopyranose residues in comparable amounts, joined into long chains by β-1,4-links.

E. Galactans

The snail *Helix pomatia* contains a polysaccharide known as galactogen which gives only galactose on hydrolysis, about one-seventh being L-galactose and the remainder D-galactose. It has a branched structure similar to amylopectin. Galactans have also been found in a few other organisms.

F. Polyuronides

These are polysaccharides that yield substantial proportions of uronic acids (see p. 70) on hydrolysis. An example is pectic acid from the pectin of fruits. This consists basically of long chains of α-1,4-linked D-galacturonic acid residues:

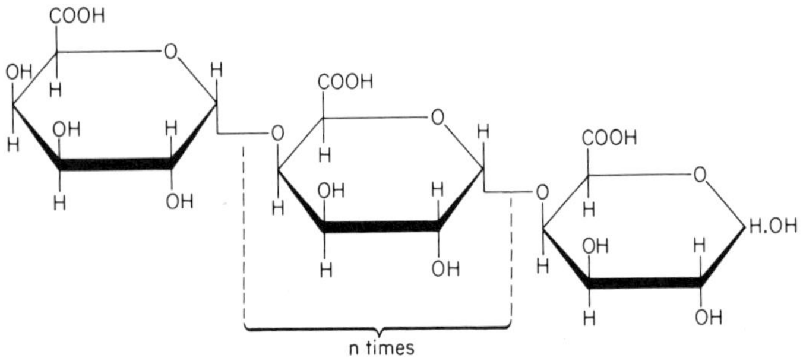

Another is alginic acid from brown seaweeds which consists of chains of β-1,4-linked mannuronic acid residues. Plant gums and mucilages are also polyuronides, and they also occur in bacteria.

G. Chitin

The shells of arthropods and molluscs are composed largely of chitin and calcium carbonate. Chitin may be isolated by soaking lobster shells in cold dilute hydrochloric acid to remove the calcium carbonate. It is fibrous like cellulose. Its structure is proved as follows:

(1) Hydrolysis with boiling acid gives equimolar amounts of acetic acid and D-glucosamine:

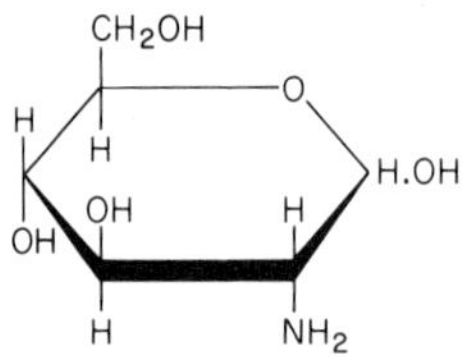

(2) Hydrolysis with an enzyme from snails' intestines give N-acetyl-glucosamine as the sole product.

(3) A disaccharide can be isolated from partial hydrolysates of chitin in which two glucosamine residues are β-1,4-linked.

(4) X-ray diffraction shows that the structure is similar to that of cellulose, and viscosity measurements show that the molecular weight is similar.

It is concluded that chitin consists of long chains of β-1,4-linked N-acetylglucosamine residues:

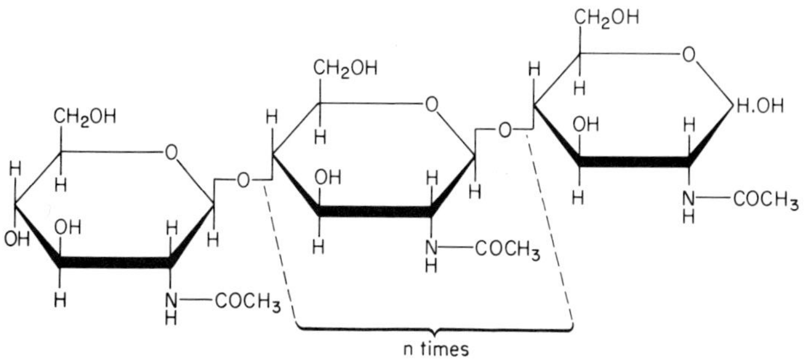

H. *Mucopolysaccharides*

These are complex polysaccharides of connective tissue and other animal tissues. An example is hyaluronic acid which consists of straight chains of alternating N-acetylglucosamine and D-glucuronic acid residues, C_1 of the former being β-linked to C_3 of the latter. Another is heparin which appears to consist of alternating residues of D-glucosamine and D-glucuronic acid; some hydroxyl residues in the molecule and all the amino groups of glucosamine are sulphated.

FURTHER READING

1. R. D. Guthrie and J. Honeyman, *An Introduction to the Chemistry of Carbohydrates*, Oxford University Press, New York, 1964.

2. E. G. V. Percival (revised by E. Percival), *Structural Carbohydrate Chemistry*, J. Garnet Miller Ltd., London, 1962.

Chapter 4

Proteins

1. Isolation of Proteins

Early in the last century a number of natural substances were isolated which had similar properties: they were amorphous powders whose solutions were coagulated by heating, or by strong acids, and all contained roughly 16% nitrogen. They included egg white, and the precipitate formed on acidifying skim milk and blood plasma, and they were named proteins. The osmotic pressures of their solutions were low, proving that their molecular weights were high; hence they could be assigned no precise molecular formulae from elementary analysis. They were given distinct names, such as casein and lactoglobulin, but how many kinds of molecule each contained was unclear. From these unpromising beginnings, a century of brilliant progress has solved the basic problems of protein structure, as will become evident in this chapter.

Through the years methods have been developed for isolating individual proteins from the mixture of proteins and other compounds in biological materials. The most useful procedures for isolating them in sufficient amounts for chemical studies are summarised below. These methods are used everyday by biochemists, largely for isolating enzymes,

all of which are proteins. Proteins are difficult to obtain pure, and usually
a series of these isolation procedures must be used. If the protein is an
enzyme, the purification is followed by measuring units of enzyme activity
in the different fractions per milligramme of protein. Because proteins are
easily denatured (see p. 123) they are usually isolated in a cold-room at
about 3°.

A. Isolations based on solubility differences

The solubility of a protein in water depends on the following factors:

(1) The presence of salts. The solubility is usually slightly greater
in dilute salt solutions than in water; but as the salt concentration is raised
the solubility soon falls below that in water and continues to fall pro-
gressively.

(2) The presence of miscible organic solvents, which lower the
solubility.

(3) The pH of the solution: the solubility varies greatly with the pH,
being minimal near the isoelectric point (see p. 103).

(4) The temperature: the solubility is usually greater at 0° than at 25°,
but with a few proteins the reverse is true.

By varying one of these factors, and keeping the others constant,
proteins can be separated from one another and from other compounds.
Most often it is the salt concentration which is varied; and usually increments of solid ammonium sulphate (chosen because it is very soluble) are

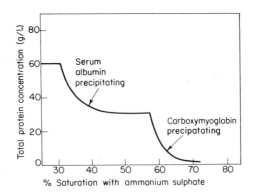

Figure 3. The addition of amonium sulphate to a solution
of serum albumin and carboxymyoglobin. (Adapted
from M. Dixon and E. C. Webb, *Advances in
Protein Chemistry*, **16** (1961), 197. Reprinted with
the permission of the authors and of Academic
Press Inc.)

dissolved in the solution, which is centrifuged after each addition to collect the precipitated proteins. Ammonium sulphate concentrations are usually expressed as percentage of saturation, saturation being 4.1 M at 25° and 3.9 M at 0°. How proteins can be fractionated in this way is illustrated by the addition of ammonium sulphate to a solution of serum albumin and carboxymyoglobin in water, each at 30g/litre. Figure 3 shows that the bulk of the serum albumin is precipitated between about 32 and 40% saturation, whereas the carboxymyoglobin remains in solution till about 58% saturation. By collecting the precipitates formed between 30 and 45, and between 55 and 70, percent saturation, the bulk of the two proteins would be separated from one another. Even in complex mixtures, each protein does largely precipitate, uninfluenced by the others, over an increment of about 10% in ammonium sulphate saturation. Figure 4 makes clear a point that is not always realised: that the percent saturation at which a protein begins to precipitate depends on its concentration. It is seen that about 3 g of carboxymyoglobin still remains in a litre of solution at 66% saturation; hence it will only start to precipitate from a solution of 3g/litre at 66% saturation.

Proteins are sometimes fractionated by changes in pH: if skimmed milk is made to pH 4.5 casein precipitates leaving the whey proteins in solution; if pancreas is homogenised in 0.25 N sulphuric acid most of the proteins precipitate, but ribonuclease remains in solution.

Proteins are also occasionally fractionated by adding organic solvents, as in the separation of blood plasma proteins by adding graded amounts of ethanol.

B. Isolation by column chromatography

In column chromatography an upright cylindrical glass tube, closed at the base with a porous glass disc, is packed with a granular material suspended in a liquid. A typical column would be 50 cm long and 2 cm diameter, but the size can be varied. The mixture of compounds to be separated is dissolved in a little of the same liquid and allowed to seep into the top of the granular bed. It is then slowly eluted (washed through) with more liquid, and the drops that emerge from the bottom of the column are collected in fractions of equal size. A granular material is chosen that has different affinities for the different components of the mixture; these components therefore require different volumes of liquid to elute them from the column, and hence are collected in different groups of tubes.

In the chromatography of proteins the granular material is usually charged, and the eluent is an aqueous buffer. Many ion-exchange resins have been tried, but the only one which works well is Amberlite IRC-50, and this with only a few proteins. More useful than resins are "cellulosic ion exchangers". They are prepared by the reaction of cellulose, suspended in alkali, with an organic halide carrying an ionisible group. Hydrogen halide is eliminated and the organic radical becomes bound by an ether linkage to some of the hydroxyls of the cellulose. Examples are the preparations of the basic diethylaminoethyl (DEAE) cellulose:

$$—OH + Cl—C_2H_4—N(C_2H_5)_2 \longrightarrow —O—C_2H_4—N(C_2H_5)_2 + HCl$$

and the acidic carboxymethyl (CM) cellulose:

$$—OH + Cl—CH_2COOH \longrightarrow —O—CH_2COOH + HCl$$

Unlike most resins, substituted celluloses do not bind proteins irreversibly, and they will fractionate larger quantities of proteins than resins. An example of such a fractionation is the elution of blood serum (30 ml) from a column of DEAE cellulose (40×2.2 cm) with Tris-phosphate buffer gradually rising in concentration from 0.005 to 0.5 M and falling in pH from 7 to 4. The serum proteins are fractionated into over sixteen peaks.

Proteins can also be isolated on columns by "molecular sieve chromatography". The columns are packed with an uncharged granular polysaccharide sold as "Sephadex". The Sephadex particles have minute spaces between the polysaccharide molecules into which inorganic ions and water molecules permeate freely, while protein molecules permeate more or less freely according to their size. The column therefore has eluent within the particles, and between them. Suppose that, in a particular column, both of these eluent volumes were 10 ml; and that a mixture of two proteins, one with very large and one with very small molecules, was eluted from the column. The large molecules will diffuse within the column into a volume of only 10 ml and hence will emerge when 10 ml of eluent has been passed through. Similarly, the small molecules will emerge at 20 ml, while molecules of intermediate size would emerge at intermediate volumes. DEAE-Sephadex can combine the virtues of ion-exchange and molecular-sieve chromatography.

C. Isolation by electrophoresis

The net charge on a protein molecule in solution changes as the pH changes (see p. 103). At any pH, molecules of different proteins carry different net charges, and this fact is made use of in separating proteins by electrophoresis. Various modifications have been devised for separating enough of a protein for chemical analysis. The simplest is electrophoresis on filter paper but better separation is achieved on gels of starch or acrylamide. Electrophoresis of these types cannot fractionate more than about one gramme of proteins.

Other methods of electrophoresis have been devised for fractionating several grammes of proteins. In one, the potential difference is applied between the vertical edges of a vertical sheet of filter paper soaked in buffer. The protein mixture is continuously run onto the top edge of the paper through a capillary, and the separated proteins continuously drip into a series of tubes beneath serrations along the bottom edge. In another, the electrophoresis is done in an upright cylindrical glass tube containing a buffer in which sucrose of gradually increasing concentration from the top to the bottom of the tube is also dissolved. The protein solution is layered on top of the buffer, and a potential difference is applied between electrodes sealed into the top and bottom of the tube. The proteins migrate down the tube, and convection currents are minimised by the density gradient of sucrose. After a while the current is turned off, and the solution drained through a stopcock in the base of the tube and collected in fractions.

It is difficult to be certain that an isolated protein is pure. The above isolation procedures themselves give some indication, since a pure protein will not be fractionated. Other methods of testing purity are small-scale paper electrophoresis, electrophoresis in the Tiselius apparatus, and sedimentation in the analytical ultracentrifuge. Purity should be tested by a number of methods and at a number of pH's. Even if there is still no fractionation, it is only possible to be certain that a protein sample is a collection of identical molecules after a single molecular structure has been proved by methods described later.

Molecular weights of proteins can be determined by a number of methods, the most important being analytical ultracentrifugation. Because protein molecules can associate by noncovalent bonds, molecular weights should be determined at a number of pH's, and the minimal values taken.

2. The Products of Protein Hydrolysis

A clue to the structure of proteins is given by the products of their hydrolysis: they can be completely converted to a mixture of low molecular weight amino acids. Some proteins also give small amounts of other compounds such as carbohydrates and lipids but, as will be seen later, these are not a fundamental part of the protein structure. This complete hydrolysis can be done by heating the protein with 6 N hydrochloric acid for twenty hours, either under reflux, or to 105° in an evacuated sealed tube—a procedure that reduces losses of some amino acids. It can also be done by incubation with a mixture of proteolytic enzymes.

Up to twenty kinds of amino acid occur in enzymic hydrolysates of proteins; their structures, names, and conventional abbreviations are shown below:

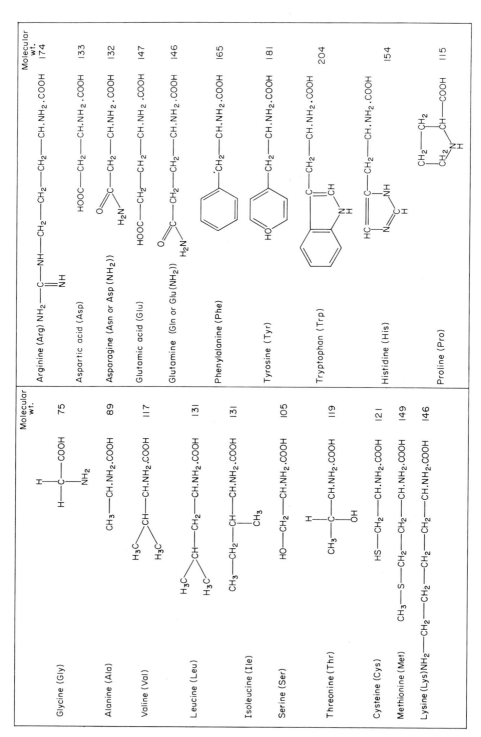

	Molecular wt.
Glycine (Gly)	75
Alanine (Ala)	89
Valine (Val)	117
Leucine (Leu)	131
Isoleucine (Ile)	131
Serine (Ser)	105
Threonine (Thr)	119
Cysteine (Cys)	121
Methionine (Met)	149
Lysine (Lys)	146

	Molecular wt.
Arginine (Arg)	174
Aspartic acid (Asp)	133
Asparagine (Asn or Asp (NH₂))	132
Glutamic acid (Glu)	147
Glutamine (Gln or Glu(NH₂))	146
Phenylalanine (Phe)	165
Tyrosine (Tyr)	181
Tryptophan (Trp)	204
Histidine (His)	154
Proline (Pro)	115

Cysteine is normally found as its oxidation product cystine:

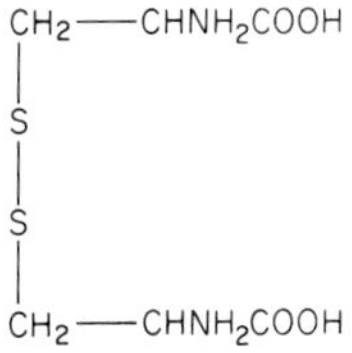

$$
\begin{array}{l}
\text{CH}_2\text{---CHNH}_2\text{COOH} \\
\quad| \\
\quad\text{S} \\
\quad| \\
\quad\text{S} \\
\quad| \\
\text{CH}_2\text{---CHNH}_2\text{COOH}
\end{array}
$$

After acid hydrolysis only up to seventeen kinds of amino acid are found because asparagine and glutamine are hydrolysed to aspartic and glutamic acids, while tryptophan decomposes. Many other amino acids occur in living organisms but only those shown have been obtained from proteins with one exception: collagen, and related proteins from connective tissue, also yield hydroxyproline and hydroxylysine:

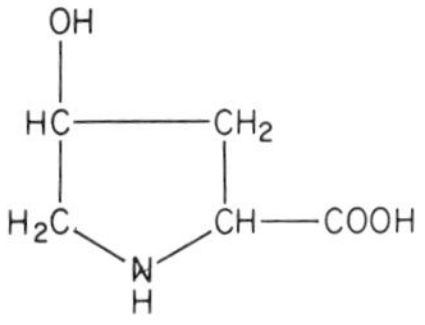

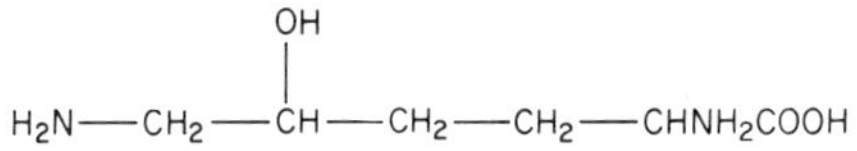

It is seen that all the amino acids except proline have the structure:

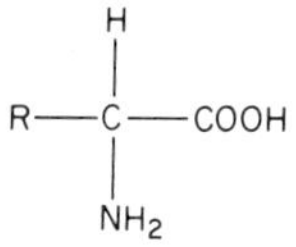

$$
\begin{array}{c}
\text{H} \\
| \\
\text{R---C---COOH} \\
| \\
\text{NH}_2
\end{array}
$$

where R is hydrogen in glycine, and an organic radical in the remainder. They are α-amino acids because the amino group is attached to the carbon adjacent to the carboxyl. Proline, though grouped with the amino acids, is in fact an imino acid; but here also one of the bonds from the nitrogen is to the α-carbon. The α-carbon of all amino acids except glycine is asymmetric. Chemical conversions have proved all protein amino acids to have the L-configuration (see p. 41) at this carbon. They are therefore represented by the projection formula:

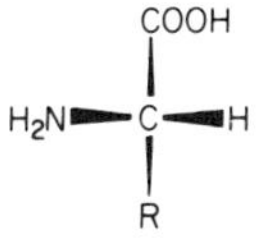

$$
\begin{array}{c}
\text{COOH} \\
| \\
\text{H}_2\text{N} \blacksquare \text{C} \blacktriangleleft \text{H} \\
| \\
\text{R}
\end{array}
$$

Proline has the same configuration at this carbon and may be represented:

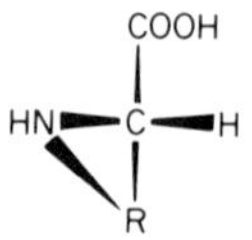

$$\begin{array}{c} \text{COOH} \\ | \\ \text{HN}\blacktriangleright\text{C}\blacktriangleleft\text{H} \\ | \\ \text{R} \end{array}$$

Threonine and isoleucine have a second asymmetric carbon. Their projection formulae, and those of their L-diastereoisomers which do not occur in proteins, are:

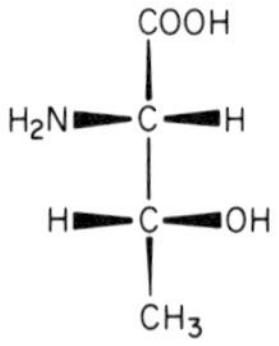

COOH	COOH	COOH	COOH
H₂N━C━H	H₂N━C━H	H₂N━C━H	H₂N━C━H
H━C━OH	HO━C━H	H₃C━C━H	H━C━CH₃
CH₃	CH₃	C₂H₅	C₂H₅
L–Threonine	L–Allothreonine	L–Isoleucine	L–Alloisoleucine

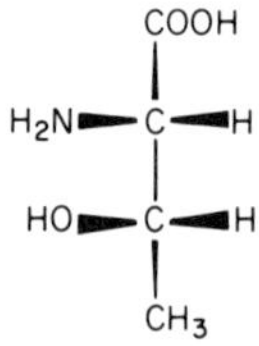

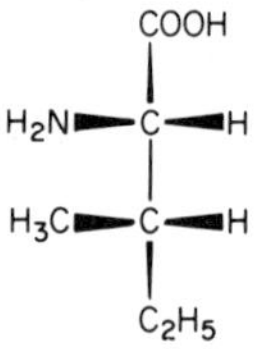

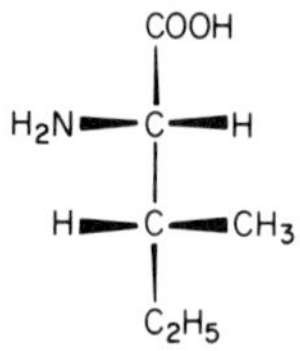

In 1902 Fischer suggested that proteins are formed from amino acids joined by peptide links. This link is illustrated in the dipeptide glycylglycine, which Fischer prepared:

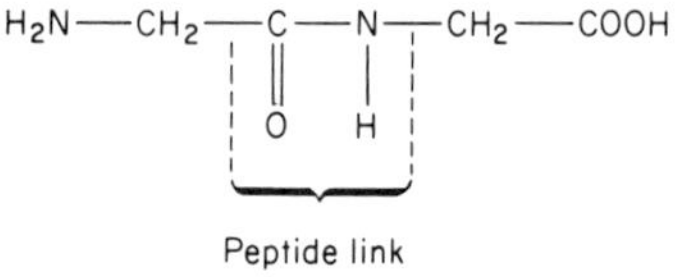

$$H_2N-CH_2-\underset{\underset{\displaystyle O}{\|}}{C}-\underset{\underset{\displaystyle H}{|}}{N}-CH_2-COOH$$

Peptide link

It is as if the carboxyl of one glycine molecule had reacted with the amino of another, with the elimination of water—although peptides cannot be readily prepared in this way. A dipeptide, just like an amino acid, has a free carboxyl and amino group, and each of these can form peptide links with the amino or carboxyl of any other amino acid. In this way three, four, five, or more amino acids can be joined to form tri-, tetra-, penta-, and polypeptides. The process can continue indefinitely since a polypeptide always has a free amino at one end of the chain and a free carboxyl at the other:

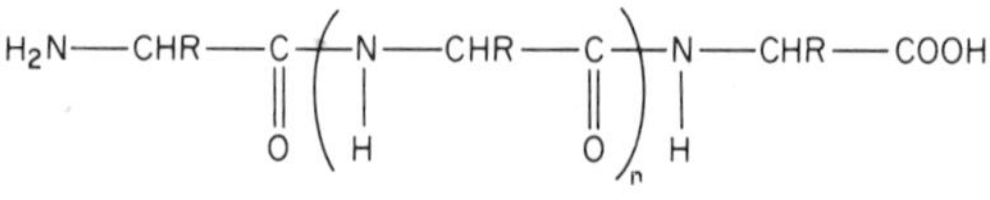

$$H_2N-CHR-\underset{\underset{\displaystyle O}{\|}}{C}\left(\underset{\underset{\displaystyle H}{|}}{N}-CHR-\underset{\underset{\displaystyle O}{\|}}{C}\right)_n\underset{\underset{\displaystyle H}{|}}{N}-CHR-COOH$$

where R is any amino acid side chain. Proline can also form peptide links with its imino group:

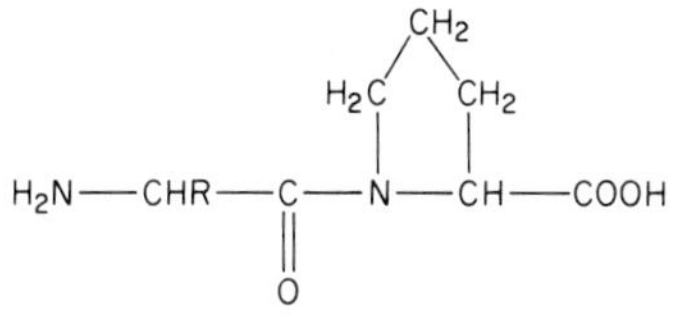

$$H_2N{-\!\!-}CHR{-\!\!-}\underset{\underset{O}{\|}}{C}{-\!\!-}N{-\!\!-}CH{-\!\!-}COOH$$

Fischer concluded that a protein molecule is either one long polypeptide or a small number of long polypeptides joined by covalent links between amino acid side chains. His evidence for this conclusion may be summarised as:

(1) Titrations show that proteins contain only a few free amino and carboxyl groups, but that they are liberated at equal rates, and in large numbers, on hydrolysis.

(2) Di-, tri-, and higher peptides can be isolated after mild acid hydrolysis of proteins.

(3) Synthetic peptides turn alkaline copper sulphate solution purple, the colour being deeper the larger the peptide (Biuret reaction). Proteins give a very deep purple.

(4) Proteolytic enzymes, such as trypsin, will also often hydrolyse synthetic peptides.

It was suggested that peptide chains in a protein molecule could be joined by the carboxyl in the side chain of a glutamic or aspartic acid residue forming a peptide-like link with the amino in the side chain of a lysine residue; or else two cysteine residues on different chains might form an —S—S— bond by the oxidation of their sulfhydryl groups:

$$R{-\!\!-}S{-\!\!-}H \;+\; H{-\!\!-}S{-\!\!-}R' \longrightarrow R{-\!\!-}S{-\!\!-}S{-\!\!-}R'$$

It will be seen later that polypeptide chains in proteins are often joined by —S—S— bonds, but that bonds between carboxyl and amino groups in side chains have not been found.

3. Properties of Amino Acids and the Synthesis of Peptides

All protein amino acids are colorless crystalline solids which dissolve easily in water, but are insoluble in alcohol and ether. The following are their principal properties:

(1) All amino acids contain at least one amino (or imino) and one carboxyl group. In strongly acid solution the amino groups are positively charged while the carboxyls are un-ionised; in strongly alkaline solution the carboxyls are negatively charged while the amino groups are un-ionised:

$$R—CH—COOH \qquad\qquad R—CH—COO^-$$
$$| \qquad\qquad\qquad\qquad |$$
$$NH_3^+ \qquad\qquad\qquad\qquad NH_2$$

Acid solution   Alkaline solution

There must be an intermediate pH at which each amino acid bears no net charge. For amino acids, such as glycine, with uncharged side chains there are two possible structures with no net charge:

$$CH_2—COO^- \qquad\qquad CH_2—COOH$$
$$| \qquad\qquad and \qquad\qquad |$$
$$NH_3^+ \quad (1) \qquad\qquad\qquad NH_2 \quad (2)$$

Aqueous solutions of amino acids have high dielectric constants, showing that the molecules have large dipole moments. This suggests that the molecules have the "zwitterion" structure (1), and measurements of Raman spectra prove this conclusively. The high melting points of amino acids, and other facts, show that in crystalline amino acids the molecuels are also zwitterions.

For each amino acid there is a characteristic pH, called the "isoionic point", at which all molecules in solution carry no net charge. For glycine it is pH 6.0 and is close to this for other amino acids with uncharged side chains. The changes in the structure of glycine from acid to alkaline solution may therefore be represented:

$$H_3N^+—CH_2—COOH \rightleftharpoons H_3N^+—CH_2—COO^- \rightleftharpoons H_2N—CH_2—COO^-$$

pH 1   pH 6.0   pH 11

At pH 1 virtually all the molecules bear a positive charge. As the pH approaches 6 an increasing proportion have the zwitterion structure until, at pH 6.0, they all have. Then, as the solution becomes alkaline an increasing proportion of the molecules bear only a negative charge.

The changes in structure with pH of amino acids that have basic or acidic side chains are more complicated. Those for aspartic acid are:

$$H_3N^+—CH—COOH \quad\rightleftharpoons\quad H_3N^+—CH—COO^- \quad\rightleftharpoons\quad H_3N^+—CH—COO^- \quad\rightleftharpoons\quad H_2N—CH—COO^-$$

with side chains:

| CH_2 | CH_2 | CH_2 | CH_2 |
| $COOH$ | $COOH$ | COO^- | COO^- |

pH 1   pH 2.8   pH 6.6   pH 11
              (Isoionic point)

At pH 1 virtually all molecules carry one positive charge. As the pH rises an increasing proportion also carry a negative charge on the α-carboxyl group until, at pH 2.8 the isoionic point, they all do. The carboxyl of the side chain is less acidic and the concentration of hydrogen ions is still sufficient to suppress its ionisation almost completely; but as the pH rises further this carboxyl also begins to ionise until, at pH 6.6 all molecules bear two negative charges and one positive charge. Finally, at pH 11, all molecules bear two negative charges. The corresponding changes with lysine are:

$$H_3N^+—CH—COOH \quad\rightleftharpoons\quad H_3N^+—CH—COO^- \quad\rightleftharpoons\quad H_2N—CH—COO^- \quad\rightleftharpoons\quad H_2N—CH—COO^-$$

| $(CH_2)_4$ | $(CH_2)_4$ | $(CH_2)_4$ | $(CH_2)_4$ |
| NH_3^+ | NH_3^+ | NH_3^+ | NH_2 |

pH 1   pH 5.6   pH 9.7   pH 11
                              (Isoionic point)

Here the amino group of the side chain is more basic than the α-amino, and it is this group which is charged at the isoionic point.

The isoionic points of proteins can now be understood. All proteins contain amino acids with basic or acidic side chains, and have a small number of terminal carboxyl and amino groups per molecule. In strongly acid solutions only the basic groups are ionised, and each protein molecule bears a number of positive charges. As the pH rises the acidic groups gain negative charges until a pH is reached at which the number of negative and positive groups are equal, and each molecule bears no net charge. This is the isoionic point and the solubility of a protein is lowest at it. The isoionic point of a protein obviously depends on its relative numbers of acidic and basic amino acids. Pepsin, for example, with a high ratio of aspartic and glutamic acids to lysine and arginine, has an isoionic point of about pH 1; histones, with a very high content of lysine and arginine, have alkaline isoionic points. The isoionic point is defined as the pH of a salt-free solution of a protein whose molecules bear no net charge, and is difficult to measure. More easily determined is the "isoelectric point" in a given buffer; namely, the pH at which the protein does not migrate in an electric field. It usually differs slightly from the isoionic point because the buffer influences the charge on the molecules.

(2) Amino acids have many of the properties expected of compounds containing amino and carboxyl groups. The amino groups can be acetylated and benzoylated, and with nitrous acid give nitrogen:

$$RCHNH_2\,COOH \;+\; HNO_2 \;\longrightarrow\; RCHOHCOOH \;+\; N_2 \;+\; H_2O$$

The Van Slyke determination of amino acids is based on the volume of nitrogen evolved in this reaction. The method has the limitation that proline, being an imino acid, does not react, while other amino groups also yield nitrogen, including those of the lysine side chains. The carboxyl groups can be esterified.

(3) When a protein amino acid (except proline) is heated with a solution of triketohydrindene hydrate (ninhydrin) it is oxidised to an aldehyde with the elimination of carbon dioxide and ammonia, while the reagent is reduced to a compound with one atom less of oxygen:

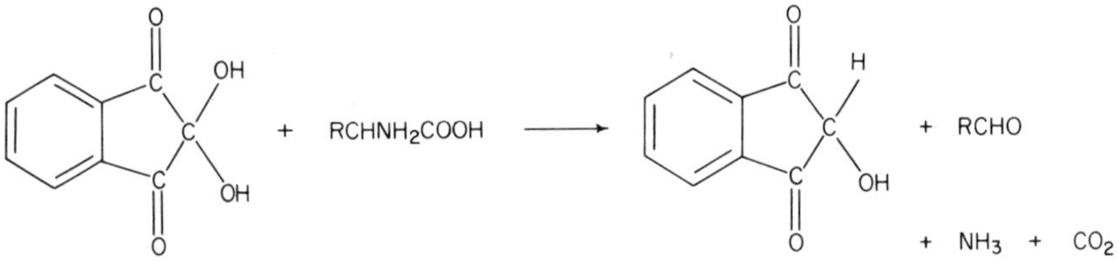

The ammonia immediately reacts with the reduced reagent and another molecule of ninhydrin to give the blue compound:

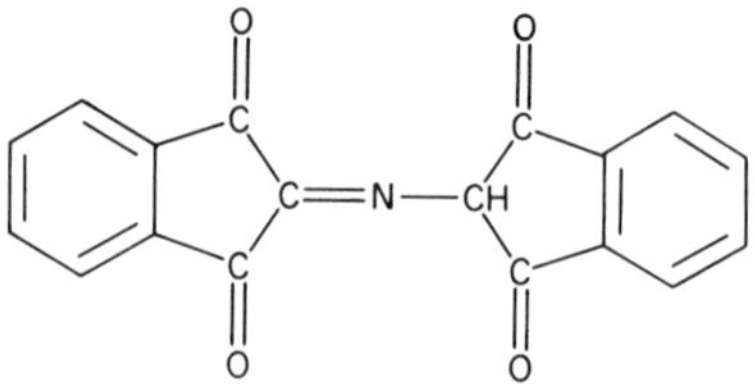

Amino acids (except proline) may be determined by measuring the evolved carbon dioxide or the intensity of the blue. The reaction is fairly specific: only compounds with an amino α to a carboxyl react in this way. Peptides and proteins react but with a lower yield of colour per residue of amino acid. Proline gives a yellow product and, in the absence of other amino acids, may be determined from this.

(4) Syntheses of peptides from amino acids basically involve the reaction of the carboxyl of one amino acid with the α-amino of another, which may be free or combined at the N-terminus of a peptide. The procedures by which this reaction can be brought about vary with the reacting amino acids, and the synthesis of peptides is a difficult and specialised occupation. Free carboxyl and amino groups do not readily react directly, and the carboxyl must first be converted to an active derivative such as an anhydride or azide. Moreover, to ensure that this active carboxyl does not react with the amino group on molecules of the same kind, the amino group must be protected: it is converted to an inactive derivative which can later be reconverted to amino under conditions that do not racemise amino acids or hydrolyse peptide links. The most useful are the carbobenzoxy and *t*-butoxycarbonyl derivatives. Carbobenzoxy chloride can be prepared by reacting benzyl alcohol with phosgene. In alkaline solution it reacts with free amino groups of amino acids and peptides to give the carbobenzoxy derivative. Carbobenzoxy groups can be removed without damage to a peptide by reduction with hydrogen and palladium:

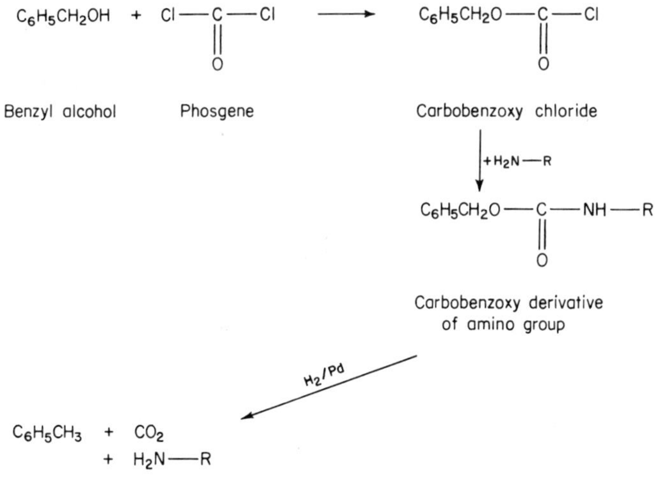

An example of the use of carbobenzoxy derivatives is in a recent synthesis of the peptide hormone angiotensin. Carbobenzoxy-L-valine was converted to an acid anhydride and reacted with the methyl ester of L-tyrosine. The product was not converted to the free dipeptide but to the acid azide which was reacted with the methyl ester of another dipeptide.

The resulting derivative of a tetrapeptide was again reacted with the methyl ester of a dipeptide to give a hexapeptide. Only then was the carbobenzoxy group removed from the original valine residue:

Cbzo —— Val + Tyr —— OMe $\xrightarrow[\text{anhydride}]{\text{Via acid}}$ Cbzo —— Val —— Tyr —— OMe

$\longrightarrow$ Cbzo ——Val——Tyr——N$_3$ $\xrightarrow{+\text{Ile —His —OMe}}$ Cbzo——Val ——Tyr ——Ile ——His —— OMe

$\xrightarrow{+\text{Pro — Phe —OMe}}$ Cbzo.Val —— Tyr —— Ile —— His —— Pro —— Phe —— OMe

$\xrightarrow{\text{H}_2/\text{Pd}}$ Val —— Tyr —— Ile —— His —— Pro —— Phe —— OMe

Reaction of the resulting methyl ester of the hexapeptide with the carbobenzoxy derivative of a dipeptide, followed by reduction to remove the carbobenzoxy group and hydrolysis to remove the methyl group, gave the octapeptide angiotensin:

$$\text{Asp—Arg—Val—Tyr—Ile—His—Pro—Phe}$$

A recent development is to link the first amino acid of the peptide to be synthesised to an insoluble resin. Only after the last amino acid has been added is the completed peptide chain removed from the resin. This method avoids the difficult isolation of a soluble intermediate after each amino acid addition, since it is merely necessary to filter off the resin and attached intermediate peptide. Insulin has been synthesised by this method.

4. The Covalent Structure of Insulin

It has been seen that a protein molecule is either a long chain of amino acids joined by peptide links, or else a few of such chains cross-linked from the side chains of certain amino acids. The next step in investigating protein structure is to select a pure protein and discover the arrangement of all the amino acids in its peptide chain or chains, together with the positions and type of any cross-linkages—that is, to determine its covalent structure. [It will be seen later (p. 115) that there is a further step beyond determining the covalent structure of a protein, namely, to determine its conformation.] Thirty years ago the possibility of discovering the covalent structure of any protein seemed very remote; and some biochemists suggested that it might prove to be impossible owing to slight variations in amino acid sequence and chain length from one molecule of a "pure" protein to the next. However, around 1945 A. C. Chibnall and F. Sanger at Cambridge University selected ox insulin, a crystalline protein of low molecular weight, and over ten years or so Sanger and his colleagues proved its covalent structure to be: (see page 108). This work proved that all the molecules of pure ox insulin are identical.

The success of this work depended very largely on Sanger's discovery of a reagent that will reveal which particular amino acid lies at the end of a peptide chain with its α-amino group uncombined (the "N-terminal" amino acid). The reagent is 2,4-dinitrofluorobenzene which, in slightly alkaline solution, reacts with the free amino groups of a protein or peptide with the elimination of hydrogen fluoride:

$$NO_2 - \hexagon - F \; + \; RNH_2 \; \longrightarrow \; NO_2 - \hexagon - \underset{H}{\overset{}{N}} - R \; + \; HF$$

When the protein is hydrolysed the dinitrophenyl groups are not removed, and amino acids which had free amino groups in the protein are obtained as dinitrophenyl (DNP) derivatives. All lysine residues acquire a DNP radical on the ε-amino group, while those that were N-terminal also acquire one on the α-amino.

The experiments which proved the covalent structure of insulin to be that shown above are summarised below.

(1) The molecular weight of insulin was shown to be 6,000 (the earliest work had suggested that it is 12,000 but this was proved to be due to association of molecules). On hydrolysis, one mole of DNP-insulin gave one mole each of DNP-glycine, DNP-phenylalanine and ε-DNP-lysine. It was concluded that each insulin molecule contains two peptide chains, one with N-terminal glycine and the other with N-terminal phenylalanine. Since lysine was obtained as ε-DNP-lysine the protein must have a single lysine residue with its ε-amino group free.

(2) It became clear that the two peptide chains of insulin are joined by —S—S— links between the side chains of cysteine residues, since the chains could be separated after oxidising the protein with performic acid. On oxidation —S—S— links are severed, the sulphur atoms being converted to sulphonic acid groups and the cysteine residues to those of cysteic acid:

$$HO_3S - CH_2 - CHNH_2 - COOH$$

When the oxidised insulin was dissolved in dilute ammonia and the solution made to pH 6.5 with acetic acid, the phenylalanyl chain precipitated leaving the glycyl chain in solution. Both of these were isolated pure and their structures investigated separately.

(3) The DNP derivatives of each chain were prepared and hydrolysed with concentrated hydrochloric acid at 37° for eight days, or with boiling 0.1 N hydrochloric acid for twelve hours. These mild conditions do not bring hydrolysis to completion, and a mixture of peptides results. Pure DNP-peptides were separated from the hydrolysates, and then hydrolysed to completion and the amino acids identified by paper chromatography. Four peptides were obtained from the glycyl chain which yielded amino acids as follows:

DNP-glycine + isoleucine
DNP-glycine + isoleucine + valine
DNP-glycine + isoleucine + valine + glutamic acid
DNP-glycine + isoleucine + valine + glutamic acid + glutamic acid

It was concluded that the sequence at the N-terminus is: Gly—Ile—Val —Glu—Glu, with the possibility that either glutamic acid residue is in fact glutamine which formed glutamic acid during the hydrolysis. Similarly, a sequence of four amino acids at the N-terminus of the phenylalanyl chain was discovered, and also a sequence of four around the lysine residue of the same chain.

(4) The two chains themselves, rather than their DNP-derivatives, were then subjected to partial acid hydrolysis to complex mixtures of peptides. Each mixture was fractionated into smaller groups of peptides by electrophoresis, by absorption of acidic and basic peptides on resins, and by absorption on charcoal of peptides containing aromatic amino acids. Pure peptides were then isolated from these groups by two-dimensional paper chromatography.

Each pure peptide was hydrolysed and its amino acid composition determined by paper chromatography. The process was then repeated with the DNP-peptide, and the N-terminal amino acid identified as the free amino acid missing from this hydrolysate—a somewhat easier procedure than identifying the DNP-amino acid directly. If the peptide contained only two amino acids its structure was then proved. For example, one peptide gave histidine and leucine on hydrolysis, while the DNP-peptide gave only leucine; hence its structure was His—Leu. From the structures of the dipeptides those of larger and larger peptides could be deduced. For example, another peptide had N-terminal serine and also contained histidine and leucine; the structure of the dipeptide just mentioned proved that this peptide was Ser—His—Leu. Again, two peptides were proved to be Leu—Val—Glu and Val—Glu—Ala. They therefore "overlap" and must come from a sequence Leu—Val—Glu—Ala in insulin.

(5) The complete sequence of each chain of insulin could not be pieced together in this way from the sequences of overlapping fragments, because the bonds between certain amino acids hydrolyse so rapidly in acid that they are never found in partial hydrolysates of proteins. Such a bond is that from the carboxyl of any amino acid residue to the amino of a serine residue. Peptides containing these sensitive sequences were obtained by hydrolysis of the two chains with the enzymes pepsin, chymotrypsin, and trypsin, and their structures determined as before. It was discovered in this work that trypsin only hydrolyses a peptide link between the carboxyl of lysine or arginine and the amino of any adjacent amino acid—a discovery which has proved very useful in later work on proteins.

It was now possible, from the known structures of overlapping peptides, to deduce the complete structures of both chains of insulin, except that it was not known which of the glutamic and aspartic acid residues were in fact glutamine and asparagine.

(6) The glutamine and asparagine residues were next identified. The two chains were hydrolysed with unspecific proteolytic enzymes to mixtures of small peptides with glutamine and asparagine undegraded. These peptides were isolated by two-dimensional paper chromatography, and those that gave glutamic or aspartic acid on acid hydrolysis were kept. Whether they in fact contained glutamine or asparagine was proved by finding whether they yielded a molecule of ammonia on acid hydrolysis, and checked by measuring their rates of migration on paper electrophoresis—peptides with glutamine or asparagine migrated more slowly than those with glutamic or aspartic acid. The positions in the insulin molecule from which these peptides came could be deduced merely from their amino acid content, since the sequence of each chain was already known.

(7) A final task remained, and it proved to be almost the hardest: to locate the disulphide bridges in insulin. The plan was to hydrolyse insulin and isolate fragments with the disulphide bridges intact. But it was found that under normal conditions of hydrolysis and isolation a random rearrangement of disulphide bonds occurred; that is, a cysteine residue in one peptide would leave its true partner and become linked to a cysteine in a different peptide. Methods of hydrolysis and isolation which avoided this were difficult to devise. Hydrolyses were finally performed in the presence of N-ethylmaleimide which inhibited the rearrangements, and peptides were separated by electrophoresis at a low temperature. Three peptides with disulphide bridges were obtained, and each was oxidised with performic acid to two peptides containing cysteic acid. The amino acid compositions of these peptides immediately revealed their origin, and hence the positions of the disulphide bridges in insulin, so completing the structure (p. 108). This structure has since been confirmed by other workers by the synthesis of insulin from amino acids.

Sanger and his colleagues also determined the structures of pig, sheep, horse, and whale insulin. These were identical to ox insulin except for amino acids 8, 9, and 10 of the glycyl chain; this sequence is —Thr—Ser —Ile— in pig and whale insulin; —Ala—Gly—Val— in sheep insulin; and —Thr—Gly—Ile— in horse insulin.

5. Present Methods of Determining Covalent Structures of Proteins

Sanger's work on insulin was soon followed by the determination of the covalent structure of ox pancreatic ribonuclease (Fig. 4) by S. Moore and W. H. Stein of Rockefeller University, and the number of proteins whose covalent structure is known is now well into two figures. The principal improvements that have taken place in chemical techniques for determining covalent structures are summarised below.

A. Amino acid composition of a protein

This can now be determined rapidly and accurately by chromatography on columns of cation-exchange resins as developed by Moore and Stein. The resins used are powdered sulphonated polystyrenes such as Dowex-50 and Amberlite IR-120. In the method originally described a chromatography column (150 cm long $\times$ 0.9 cm diameter) enclosed in a waterjacket at 50° is filled with a suspension of the resin in sodium citrate buffer (0.2 N; pH 3.25). The protein hydrolysate in a few milliliters of buffer is allowed to seep into the top of the column, and is then slowly eluted with the citrate buffer, the pH of which is raised to 4.25 after 250 ml. The amino acids emerge separately from the column after characteristic volumes of eluent have passed through. The eluent may be collected in small factions and the amino acid content of each determined by the ninhydrin method (see p. 104); the quantity of each amino acid is then found by summation of the amounts in adjacent tubes. Alternatively a fully automatic machine may be used in which the eluent leaving the column is continuously mixed with ninhydrin reagent, and the intensity of the resulting blue colour is automatically plotted against the volume of eluent. A series of peaks is obtained and the area under each peak is proportional to the quantity of the amino acid which is known to emerge at that volume. In this original procedure lysine, histidine, and arginine are so firmly bound by the resin that they must be separately determined on columns 15 cm long, but subsequent modifications enable all amino acids to be determined with one column.

Small amounts of serine, threonine, and cysteine are destroyed during acid hydrolysis of proteins, while valine and isoleucine are released more slowly than other amino acids. Hence, amino acid analyses must be made

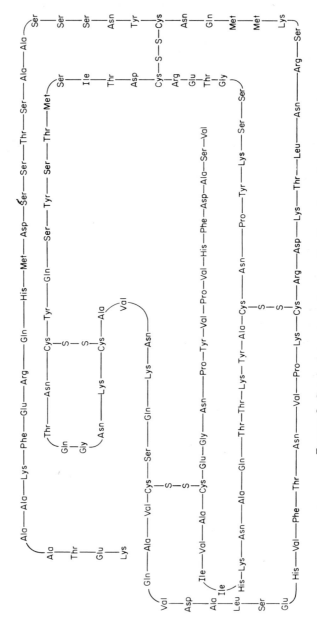

Figure 4. Covalent structure of pancreatic ribonuclease of ox.

after various times of hydrolysis (usually 24, 48, 72, and 96 hours) and the concentrations of these amino acids deduced by extrapolation backwards or forwards. Tryptophan is completely destroyed on acid hydrolysis and must be separately determined in an alkaline hydrolysate. The automatic analyser will determine all amino acids in a protein hydrolysate with an accuracy of $100 \pm 3\%$. This accuracy makes it possible to determine the number of residues of each amino acid per molecule of a protein from its amino acid analysis, provided the molecular weight is not too large. For example, Moore and Stein found that each molecule of ribonuclease of weight 14,000, contained 3.05 residues of glycine, 2.97 of phenylalanine, and 8.95 of valine. It was clear that the true values were 3,3, and 9.

B. Enzymic digestion

Most of Sanger's work was done on peptides isolated from the complex mixture formed on mild acid hydrolysis of insulin. Nowadays proteins are usually hydrolysed into a simpler mixture of peptides by enzymes that are more or less specific for certain links. The most useful are trypsin which only hydrolyses peptide links between the carboxyl group of lysine or arginine and the amino group of another amino acid; chymotrypsin which is less specific, but hydrolyses most rapidly links involving the carboxyls of tyrosine, phenylalanine, and tryptophan; and pepsin which is less specific still but hydrolyses most rapidly links on each side of phenylalanine and tyrosine residues. To facilitate enzymic digestion, disulphide bonds in the protein must first be cleaved, either by oxidation with performic acid or by reduction.

The work on ribonuclease provides an example of the use of enzymes. Analysis showed ribonuclease to contain ten lysine and four arginine residues. On digestion of oxidised ribonuclease with trypsin thirteen peptides were formed, and these were isolated by chromatography on columns of Dowex-50. (Two of the peptides contained two lysine residues, one lysine in each being resistant to hydrolysis.) Four of these peptides were too large for their structures to be determined directly, and they were first broken into smaller fragments with chymotrypsin and pepsin. The structures of all these peptides were then determined; but the amino acid sequence of ribonuclease could not immediately be deduced, since the order in which these peptides occurred in the molecule was unknown. This was discovered by digesting ribonuclease with chymotrypsin and pepsin, and isolating "bridge" peptides. These contained the links severed by trypsin, and hence always contained the C-terminal amino acids of one tryptic peptide and the N-terminal ones of the adjacent one. Amino acid analysis of these bridge peptides sufficed to show which tryptic peptides had been neighbours in ribonuclease.

C. Determination of amino acid sequences

A great advance has been the development of the reaction described in 1950 by P. Edman in which the N-terminal amino acid of a peptide is removed yielding a peptide one amino acid shorter. The series of reactions is as follows:

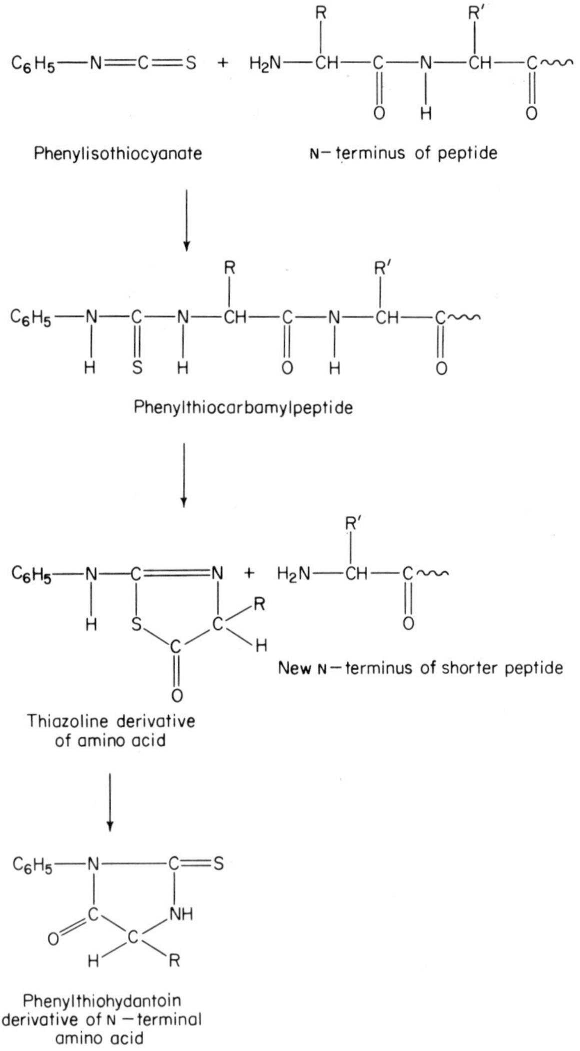

Phenylisothiocyanate — N-terminus of peptide

Phenylthiocarbamylpeptide

Thiazoline derivative of amino acid — New N-terminus of shorter peptide

Phenylthiohydantoin derivative of N-terminal amino acid

The peptide is treated with phenylisothiocyanate in a volatile alkaline buffer to form the phenylthiocarbamyl peptide. Excess reagent is then extracted with a solvent—and in this step lies the beauty of the procedure,

114

since further reaction is prevented when the new N-terminal amino acid is next exposed. The buffer is then removed by freeze-drying and the residue dissolved in an acid solution, whereupon the N-terminal amino acid is released as the thiazoline (reduced thiazole) derivative. This spontaneously rearranges to a phenylthiohydantoin which is extracted with an organic solvent. Which particular amino acid has been removed may be found either by identifying the particular phenylthiohydantoin, or more simply by comparing the amino acid composition of the residual peptide with that of the original peptide. The residual peptide can then be submitted to a further Edman degradation. In theory this cycle could be repeated until all amino acids were identified; in practice, it is seldom possible to identify more than four or five amino acids at the N-terminus owing to difficulties in the procedure. One of these is that the optimum conditions vary with the peptide and cannot be predicted, and hence low yields often result. Also, acid-labile seryl and threonyl bonds may be hydrolysed, while N-terminal glutamine residues may inhibit further reaction by cyclising to pyrrolidonecarboxylic acid residues:

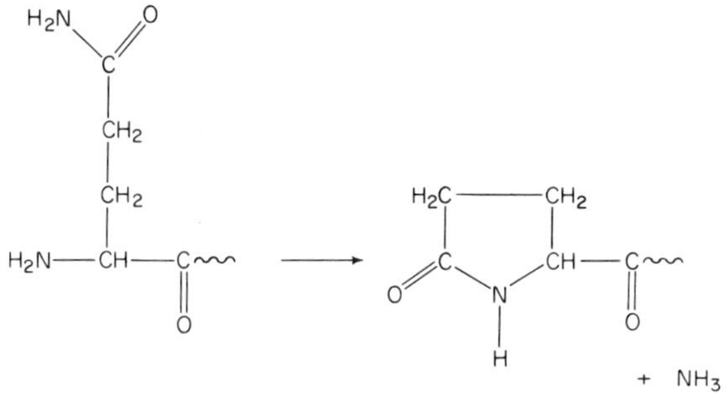

Aminopeptidase can also be useful for determining sequences at N-termini, particularly if the Edman degradation has failed. This enzyme removes the N-terminal amino acid of a peptide molecule, but immediately proceeds to do the same to the shorter peptide so formed. Therefore, samples must be taken at intervals from the digest and the free amino acids identified in the hope of discovering the order in which they are released. This is difficult if an amino acid that is rapidly hydrolysed succeeds one that is slowly hydrolysed. Carboxypeptidases A and B can similarly be used to determine C-terminal sequences.

6. Protein Conformation

The structure of a protein is not fully defined by its covalent structure since this could exist in a very large number of conformations (see p. 12) as the result of the rotation of the component groups about single bonds,

The biological properties of a protein appear to result from its being arranged in one particular conformation, and when this is destroyed by denaturing agents those properties are lost.

The foundation of our approach to protein conformation was laid by Linus Pauling and his colleagues at the California Institute of Technology around 1950. They proceeded on the assumption that peptide chains will

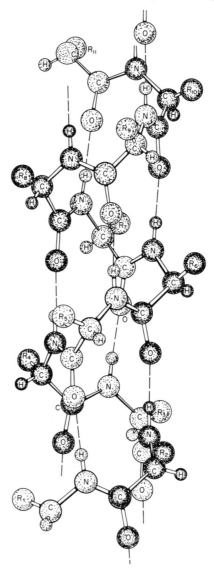

Figure 5. Peptide chain of 11 L-amino acids in right-handed α-helix. The dotted lines represent hydrogen bonds.

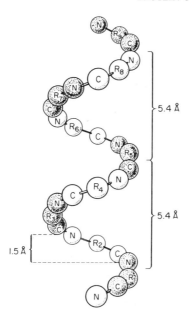

Figure 6. Dimensions of the α-helix.

spontaneously assume their most stable conformation, and set about finding this by building accurate molecular models, based on X-ray diffraction measurements of bond lengths and angles in amino acids and peptides. These models they arranged, without distortion of bond angles, into conformations that would be stabilised by hydrogen bonds between the carbonyl and imino groups of the peptide bonds. They concluded that the most stable structure for a chain of L-amino acids was a right-handed helix—the dissymmetric structure of a household corkscrew. The most stable of a number of possible helical structures was the "α-helix" and details of it are shown in Figures 5 and 6. It is seen that the carbonyl group of each peptide bond is hydrogen bonded to the imino group of the fourth amino acid away from it:

$$-\overset{O}{\overset{\|}{C}}-(NH-CHR-CO)_3-\overset{H}{\overset{|}{N}}-$$

It follows that at least three hydrogen bonds must be broken before free rotation can occur between any of the atoms of the chain, a fact which gives the helix considerable stability. The six atoms of each peptide group (C—CO—NH—C) lie in a plane as a result of the carbonyl carbon being partially double bonded to the imino nitrogen owing to resonance. It was concluded that the most stable structure for a chain of D-amino acids is a left-handed α-helix—the mirror image of a household corkscrew.

The proposed α-helix was immediately supported by certain previously unexplained X-ray diffraction patterns given by proteins, and the
evidence is now conclusive that it occurs extensively in proteins and
synthetic peptides. For example, X-ray diffraction measurements of
fibres of the synthetic peptide poly-L-alanine show that the chains have a
repeating characteristic at every 1.5 Å, the distance between successive
amino acid residues in the α-helix, and at every 5.4 Å, the distance between
successive turns of the helix (see Fig. 6). These measurements also show
that the helixes are right-handed. X-ray diffraction also shows that un-
stretched fibres of hair, horn, and wool are composed of molecules of the
protein keratin arranged lengthways, again with a repeat at 1.5 Å, but with
another at 5.1 Å rather than 5.4 Å. These values appear to result from
α-helical keratin molecules being twisted together lengthways like the
strands of a cable. The dissymmetry of the α-helix causes solutions of
molecules that contain it to rotate the plane of polarised light, and it is
possible from optical rotatory dispersion measurements (see p. 25) to
calculate the proportion of the peptide chain of a globular protein which is
α-helical. It is found that most globular proteins have 20 to 80% of their
peptide chains as α-helixes.

The α-helix is not the only regular way in which peptide chains can
be arranged. For example, X-ray measurements show that silk fibres, and
stretched hair and other keratin fibres, have a repeat at 6.9 Å which is
almost the 7.2 Å which would be found in a fully extended peptide chain:

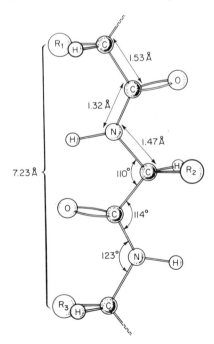

It appears that the peptide chains are in fact almost fully extended, and bound together by hydrogen bonds between adjacent chains to form parallel or antiparallel "pleated sheets":

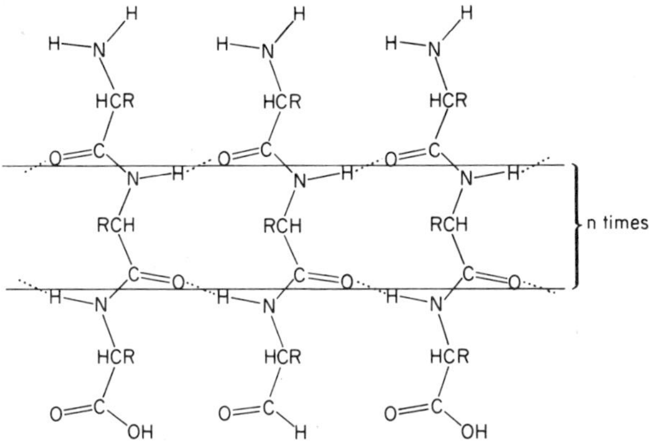

Parallel
C-termini all at one end, N-termini at other
Dotted lines represent hydrogen bonds)

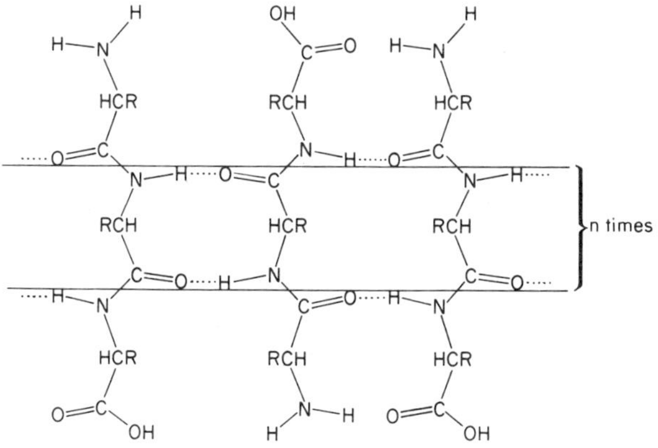

Antiparallel
(C-termini and N-termini alternate at both ends)

The protein conformations that have been described so far are primarily stabilized by bonds between groups in the backbone of the peptide chain, rather than in the amino acid side chains. Such conformations are known as the "secondary" structures of proteins in a classification in which covalent structures are "primary", and structures that result from further coiling of the secondary structures into ones bound together by bonds between amino acid side chains are "tertiary". This classification is not altogether desirable since it suggests clear-cut distinctions which do not usually exist. For example, the α-helix is a typical secondary structure and hence should be uninfluenced by amino acid side chains, but experiments with synthetic peptides show that it is not. Thus, optical rotation and other properties show that molecules of polyglutamic acid exist in acid solutions as α-helixes, but in alkaline solutions as random coils:

Acid   Alkaline

Polylysine behaves in the opposite way, existing as α-helixes in alkaline solution and as random coils in acid. In these peptides the α-helix is unstable when the amino acid side chains are charged. Rather than to speak of primary, secondary, and tertiary, it seems better merely to subdivide protein structure into covalent structure and conformation, and this is increasingly being done.

Most proteins are not fibrous but "globular": physical measurements show that their molecules are spheroid. Our knowledge of the conformation of globular proteins has been greatly advanced in the last few years by the X-ray diffraction analysis of myoglobin, hemoglobin, lysozyme, pancreatic ribonuclease and papain. The myoglobin molecule is a single chain of 151 amino acids associated with a heme group (see p. 180) which can bind oxygen. The folding of the peptide chain in crystalline myoglobin has been deduced from X-ray diffraction measurements by J. C. Kendrew and his colleagues at Cambridge University. The straight regions of the peptide chain are right-handed α-helixes and contain about 77% of the amino acids. The other regions contain all the proline residues, since these will not fit into α-helixes. The coiling of the peptide chain cannot be stabilised by covalent bonds, since myoglobin contains no cysteine residues to form disulfide bonds. It appears that the coiling of this and other globular proteins is stabilised by hydrogen bonds, ionic bonds, and hydrophobic bonds between amino acid side chains. By hydrophobic bonding is meant the tendency of nonpolar groups in an aqueous medium to aggregate, in the way that the hydrocarbon chains of higher fatty acids aggregate to form micelles. The side chains of valine, leucine, isoleucine, and phenylalanine tend to aggregate in this way. The heme group of myoglobin is also bound by amino acids with nonpolar side chains which

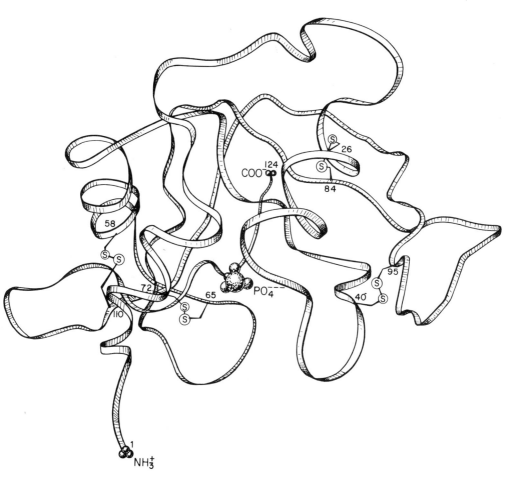

Figure 7. Conformation of pancreatic ribonuclease of ox. The
N-terminus (amino acid 1) and C-terminus (amino
acid 124) and the cysteine residues which form
disulphide bridges have been numbered. The site
of enzyme activity is where a phosphate ion is
shown to be bound. (By kind permission of Dr. D.
Harker and Dr. E. Kartha.)

form hydrophobic bonds with the nonpolar groups of the heme.

The molecule of the enzyme hen egg-white lysozyme is a single chain of amino acids of known covalent structure. X-ray measurements of D. C. Phillips and colleagues in London revealed the conformation of this protein. About 55 of its 129 amino acids lie in about six separate lengths of α-helix. Measurements on complexes of the protein with molecules that act as competitive inhibitors of its enzyme action have shown which part of the enzyme probably reacts with the substrate. This active site includes amino acids from different parts of the polypeptide chain which come together in the natural conformation. Figure 7 shows the conformation of pancreatic ribonuclease deduced by D. Harker and colleagues of Buffalo, New York. It differs from myoglobin and lysozyme in having very few amino acids in α-helixes.

M. F. Perutz and his colleagues at Cambridge University have shown that hemoglobin molecules are composed of two "α" peptide chains of identical conformation, and two identical "β" chains. These four chains are not bound by covalent links, as are the two peptide chains of insulin, but by noncovalent bonds similar to those which stabilise the folding of the peptide chain of myoglobin. (The association of separate peptide chains in this way is sometimes called the "quaternary" structure of a protein.) The amino acid sequences are identical along short lengths of the α- and β-chains. X-ray diffraction shows that both chains have conformations very similar to that of myoglobin. In the hemoglobin molecule the contours of the two α-chains exactly fit into those of the two β-chains so allowing the formation of many noncovalent bonds. This demonstration of how four peptide chains can be bound into a larger molecule by noncovalent bonds is important since it suggests how the different macromolecules which are synthesised in a living cell could spontaneously assemble into the different cell structures such as ribosomes and cell membranes. It is probable that such macromolecules collide together until they find their correct neighbours into which they fit and bind. It thus also becomes clear that there is no distinct dividing line between macromolecules and cell particles.

Each of the four heme groups of hemoglobin can bind one molecule of oxygen. The oxygen dissociation curve of hemoglobin is sigmoid, showing that when it has bound one mole of oxygen its affinity for oxygen increases. Since the heme groups in hemoglobin are over 25 Å apart there can be no simple interaction by which a heme group which has bound oxygen increases the affinity of the three neighbouring heme groups for oxygen. Perutz has shown that in hemoglobin that has bound one mole of oxygen the conformation of the protein is slightly changed, and it is apparently this change which increases the affinity of the remaining heme groups for oxygen. Effects of this type, in which an atom or molecule being bound at one site on a protein causes a change in affinity for another atom or molecule at another site on the protein, are known as "allosteric effects", and are very important in the regulation of the affinities of enzymes for their substrates. They all appear to result from the binding of the first molecule altering the conformation of the enzyme and, as a result, its affinity for the second molecule.

It appears that a protein, provided it is not denatured, retains in solution more or less the same conformation it has in the solid. Thus, optical rotation measurements on solutions of myoglobin suggest that about 73% of the amino acids are in α-helixes in agreement with the 77% suggested by X-ray diffraction measurements of the crystalline protein. Also, the fact that a globular protein can be crystallised suggests that its molecules in solution all have an identical rigid structure. However, the noncovalent association between peptide chains in solution can be modified by slight changes in pH. Thus in mildly acid solution the molecular weight of hemoglobin halves, showing that there are now only two peptide chains per molecule. Molecular weight measurements also show that the molecules of a protein often associated with one another by noncovalent attractions to give dimers at certain pH's or ionic strengths.

Under certain extreme conditions the specific conformation of a protein in solution is destroyed to give a mixture of molecules of assorted conformations, and the characteristic properties of the protein, such as its catalytic ability, are lost. This process is known as denaturation. It is usually irreversible but occasionally the molecules can regain their original conformation under the correct conditions. High temperatures and extremes of pH will denature protein solutions as will the addition of urea.

FURTHER READING

1. P. Alexander, R. J. Block and H. P. Lundgren, editors, *A Laboratory Manual of Analytical Methods of Protein Chemistry*, Pergamon Press, Oxford, vols. 1 and 2, 1960. vol. 3, 1961; vol. 4, 1966. A comprehensive treatise by many authors dealing with practical techniques for investigating proteins.

2. M. Dixon and E. C. Webb, *Enzyme Fractionation by Salting-Out: A Theoretical Note*, Advances in Protein Chemistry, **16** (1961) 197. Should be read by anyone who contemplates isolating proteins.

3. M. Florkin and E. H. Stotz, editors, *Comprehensive Biochemistry*, Elsevier Publishing Co., Amsterdam, 1962–1965. A sixteen-volume work by many authors. Especially good on the structure of biological compounds. Proteins are comprehensively dealt with in volumes 7 and 8.

4. R. F. Steiner, *The Chemical Foundations of Molecular Biology*, Van Nostrand Co., Princeton, New Jersey, 1965. Structure of proteins discussed in detail.

Chapter 5

Nucleic Acids

1. Isolation of Nucleic Acids

Like proteins, nucleic acids were isolated from living organisms in the last century as amorphous powders. Because they had similar properties, such as insolubility in acids, and similar compositions with about 9% phosphorus, they were given the common name of nucleic acids—"nucleic" because cell nuclei contain high concentrations. But elementary analyses gave few clues to their structure, and it was unclear how many kinds of molecule were present in any sample of nucleic acid.

Again, a century of experimentation has clarified the basic principles of nucleic acid structure, but our knowledge is less complete than it is of protein structure. This difference is largely a result of the higher molecular weights of nucleic acids. Nucleic acids are of two kinds: deoxyribonucleic acids and ribonucleic acids. (These are abbreviated to DNA and RNA, although DNA's and RNA's would be more appropriate since there are, of course, many kinds of each.) Any living cell appears to contain only one or a few very large DNA molecules. For example, a T_2 bacterial virus contains only a single DNA molecule of weight about 1×10^8, while an *E. coli* cell contains a single molecule of weight about 2×10^9. Cells of higher organisms appear to contain only a few DNA molecules of similar size. To determine the complete covalent structure of DNA molecules of this size is at present inconceivable. At least three distinct types of RNA occur in all living cells. They are transfer RNA (tRNA—also known as soluble or supernatent RNA) which is dissolved in the cytoplasm and makes up about 15% of the total RNA of most cells; ribosomal RNA (rRNA) which occurs in cytoplasmic particles named ribosomes and makes up about 80% of the total RNA; and messenger RNA (mRNA), which is the least clearly characterised, and occurs in small amounts. Transfer RNA's have molecular weights around 25,000 and some have been isolated pure and their covalent structures determined. But messenger RNA's and the main components of ribosomal RNA have molecular weights of 500,000 and up, and the possibility of determining their complete structures is remote.

The principal methods of isolating RNA and DNA will now be summarised. In living organisms DNA, and most kinds of RNA, are bound to proteins by ionic linkages, and the basic step in their isolation is their separation from proteins. This is usually done with organic solvents, detergents or phenol which denature and precipitate proteins leaving nucleic acids in solution. The products of nucleic acid isolation are almost always mixtures of RNA's or DNA's of different structure. Isolations are best done at low temperatures and near neutrality to minimise changes in covalent structure and conformation. Solutions should always contain electrolytes since conformations of nucleic acids can be disrupted by distilled water. Most tissues contain enzymes that hydrolyse nucleic acids and it is often necessary to add compounds that inhibit them. Mechanical blending lowers the molecular weight of DNA and should be minimised, but some degradation always occurs: the DNA molecules of *E. coli*, for example, are about 1 mm long and even hand stirring breaks them.

Pure DNA isolated by these procedures is a white fibrous solid. It is insoluble in water but will dissolve slowly in dilute salt solutions— "dilute saline citrate" (0.015 M sodium chloride + 0.0015 M sodium citrate) is normally used. Pure RNA tends to be less fibrous and more readily soluble.

A. Isolation of RNA

The methods most commonly used involve extractions with phenol and water. The original phenol method was introduced in 1956 by K. S. Kirby. The tissue homogenate was stirred for one hour with a mixture of phenol and water and then centrifuged. At room temperature mixtures of phenol and water separate into two layers: an upper "aqueous" layer, which is a solution of about 10% phenol in water, and a lower "phenol" layer which is a solution of about 25% water in phenol. RNA and poly-saccharides were found in the aqueous layer, some protein at the liquid:liquid "interphase" and DNA and more protein at the bottom of the tube:

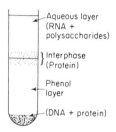

The aqueous layer was removed by suction and the RNA and some poly-saccharides precipitated by adding ethanol. The precipitate was dissolved in a phosphate buffer, 2-methoxyethanol added, and the mixture shaken. Two immiscible phases were formed, and RNA dissolved completely in the upper phase which contained the higher proportion of methoxy-ethanol, leaving polysaccharides in the lower phase. The upper phase was removed and dialysed against water. The solution was then made to 2% with potassium acetate and the RNA precipitated by adding 2 volumes of ethanol. The precipitate was separated, washed with aqueous ethanol, and dried.

Since 1956 the method has been considerably refined. Inhibitors of ribonuclease have been added, and modifications have been devised that will separate transfer, ribosomal, and messenger RNA free from poly-saccharides.

B. Isolation of DNA

Methods either involve removal of proteins with detergents and organic solvents, or with phenol. A good method for isolating DNA from bacteria was devised by J. Marmur, and it can be adapted for animal tissues. The bacteria are suspended in saline containing ethylenediaminetetra-acetate (EDTA) at pH 8, and a solution of the detergent sodium dodecyl sulphate is added. The EDTA binds divalent metal ions required by DNAase enzymes, which also have low activity at pH 8. The detergent lyses the cells and denatures some proteins, and the solution becomes viscous from liberated DNA. It is shaken for thirty minutes with an equal volume of a mixture of chloroform and isoamyl alcohol to denature proteins. An emulsion is formed which is then separated into upper and lower layers, and an interphase, by centrifuging. The upper aqueous layer, which contains the DNA and RNA is removed, leaving a large part of the proteins behind. Two volumes of ethanol are layered onto the solution which is then slowly mixed with a glass rod. The DNA and RNA precipitate as threads which gather as a spool on the rod. The precipitate is redissolved in saline, again shaken with chloroform and isoamyl alcohol, and again isolated from the upper layer. This procedure is repeated until little protein separates at the interphase. The solution of DNA and RNA is now incubated with ribonuclease. This digestion of RNA liberates more proteins which are removed by further shakings with chloroform and isoamyl alcohol. DNA is then precipitated as before and finally re-precipitated with isopropanol. The yield of DNA is about 50%. Preparations of DNA have also been devised by extraction with aqueous phenol containing detergents and other reagents.

2. Fractionation of Nucleic Acids

Samples of RNA and DNA may be separated into fractions of different composition by the methods outlined below, but only certain transfer RNA's have been obtained chemically pure.

A. Fractionation of RNA by column chromatography

The columns most used contain the inert powder kieselguhr coated with a basic protein whose positive side chains attract the negatively charged nucleic acid. Originally the columns were coated with histones, but it is more convenient to use crystalline blood serum albumin, previously converted into a basic protein by neutralising the carboxyl groups of its aspartic and glutamic acid residues by methylation. The serum albumin (5 gm) is simply added to absolute methanol (500 ml) containing 4.2 ml of 12 N hydrochloric acid. The protein dissolves and the methylated albumin later precipitates. A 1% solution in water is added to a suspension of kieselguhr in buffered saline. The protein precipitates on the particles which are then poured into the column. The mixture of RNA is eluted from the column with solutions of sodium chloride of increasing concentration, and RNA in the effluent is determined by its ultraviolet extinction. RNA's emerge in order of increasing molecular weight. Transfer RNA comes first, usually in one peak, but conditions can be devised which give a number of peaks. Ribosomal RNA always gives two peaks. Columns of substituted celluloses and of Sephadex are also used to fractionate RNA.

B. *Fractionation of RNA by density gradient centrifugation*

Transfer RNA and two components of ribosomal RNA can be separated into three peaks by this method. A 20-ml plastic centrifuge tube is filled with a sucrose solution, buffered at pH 5, that continuously increases in concentration (and hence in density) from 5% at the top to 20% at the bottom. The RNA is layered on top of the sucrose and centrifuged at around $100,000 \times G$. The RNA's sediment at speeds which vary with their molecular size and conformation and the centrifuge is stopped after about sixteen hours before any have reached the bottom of the tube. A hole is pierced in the base of the tube and the emerging drops are collected in fractions, and their RNA concentrations determined by ultraviolet extinction. The two ribosomal RNA components emerge first and the transfer RNA last. Density gradient separation can be performed on a larger scale with a zonal ultracentrifuge, and alternative compounds to sucrose have been introduced.

C. *Fractionation of RNA by countercurrent distribution*

Chemically pure components of transfer RNA have been isolated by this method. The fractionation depends on differences in the partition coefficients of RNA's between two immiscible solvents. It was seen (p. 127) that when RNA in a phosphate buffer is shaken with 2-methoxyethanol it passes completely into the upper phase which contains the higher proportion of methoxyethanol. The composition of the two phases can be modified so that the RNA's partition more or less evenly between the two phases. The value of countercurrent distribution over column chromatography, in fact, lies in this ability to modify both phases until the best separation between components is achieved.

The countercurrent apparatus consists of a series of interconnected glass tubes (usually between 50 and 500 of about 5 ml capacity) each of which acts as a separating funnel. Each tube is half filled with the lower phase of the two immiscible solvents and the RNA, dissolved in the upper phase, is added to the first tube. The apparatus is shaken till the RNA's in the first tube partition between the phases. The apparatus is then tipped so that the upper phase of the first tube is added to the second while fresh upper phase, containing no RNA, is drawn into the first. The shaking and transferring are continued until the upper phase reaches the last tube (or sometimes the separation is continued by running the upper phase out of the apparatus and collecting it in tubes). A solvent is then added to each tube to give one phase and each is assayed for RNA. Different RNA's are found in different groups of tubes, since the rate at which they travel along the apparatus depends on their solubility in the upper phase. This solubility tends to increase with the adenine content. RNA can also be fractionated by electrophoresis.

D. Fractionation of DNA

Samples of DNA can be separated into fractions of different molecular weight and composition by elution, with solutions of increasing salt concentration, from columns of substituted cellulose, or of methylated albumin on kieselguhr. They can also be fractionated on density gradients formed by centrifuging concentrated solutions of cesium chloride at about $100,000 \times G$ for about twenty hours. At this force the cesium chloride molecules move towards the base of the tube, forming a gradient of density from the top to the bottom. If a sample of DNA is mixed with the solution before centrifuging the different molecules move to regions of the tube in which the density of the solution equals their density. After centrifuging, the tube is pierced at the base and the solution collected in fractions. The density of DNA is greater the greater the content of guanine and cytosine (see p. 134); this content can therefore be determined from the density of the solution in which the DNA comes to rest. DNA can also be fractionated by countercurrent distribution.

3. Purines and Pyrimidines and Their Determination

Clues to the structure of nucleic acids are given by their hydrolysis products. Under the correct conditions (see Figures 8 and 9) both DNA and RNA can be hydrolysed to low molecular weight products of three kinds: a pentose sugar; purines and pyrimidines; and phosphoric acid. It is seen that DNA and RNA differ in their ease of acid and alkaline hydrolysis; this can be explained by a structural difference (see p. 144). The pentose from RNA is always D-ribose and that from DNA is always 2-deoxy-D-ribose (see p. 69). Figure 10, p. 133 shows structures of the principal purines and pyrimidines (often called "bases" because they contain basic nitrogen atoms). They are systematically named as if derived from the parent compounds pyrimidine and purine by the replacement of hydrogen atoms by hydroxyl, amino, and methyl groups. Uracil, for example, is 2,4-dihydroxypyrimidine:

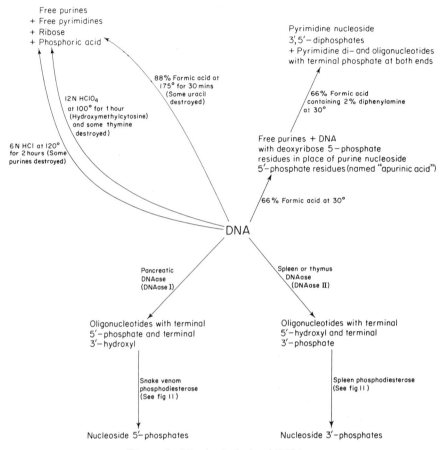

Figure 8. The hydrolysis of DNA.

It has however been proved that in hydroxylated pyrimidines and purines a hydrogen atom migrates from the hydroxyl to the adjacent nitrogen with the formation of a keto group. For example, the spectra of 2-hydroxy-pyrimidine correspond with those of its N-methyl rather than its O-methyl derivative:

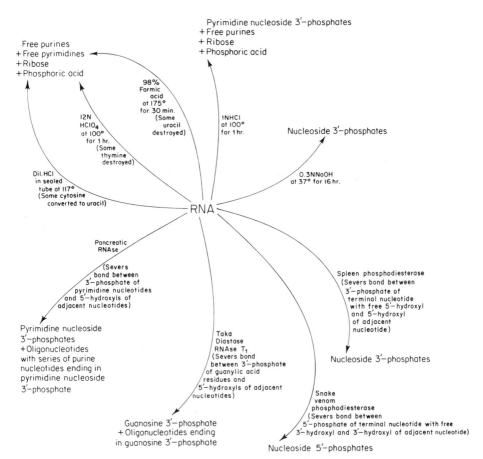

Figure 9. The hydrolysis of RNA.

Hence the true structure of uracil is that in Figure 10. By similar methods it has been shown that the amino derivatives do not undergo a similar change to imino derivatives.

DNA's on complete hydrolysis always yield adenine, guanine, and thymine; all also yield cytosine except DNA's of certain bacteriophages which give 5-hydroxymethylcytosine. DNA's of higher animals and plants also give 5-methylcytosine as about 6% of the total bases, while bacterial DNA usually yields a few percent of 6-methylaminopurine. RNA's always yield adenine, guanine, cytosine, and uracil, while certain RNA's notably transfer RNA, also give other "minor" bases in smaller amounts (Fig. 10, p. 133).

The total number of base molecules formed on hydrolysis of a sample of RNA or DNA, equals the number of ribose or deoxyribose molecules,

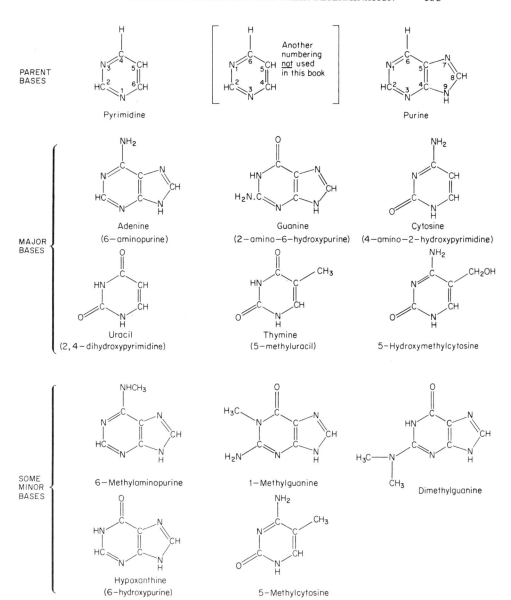

Figure 10. The principle purines and pyrimidines of nucleic acids.

and the number of phosphoric acid molecules. Hence the hydrolysis products of one sample of RNA or DNA only differ from those of another in the relative numbers of the different bases. This "base composition" is usually determined by paper chromatography of an acid hydrolysate of the nucleic acid. A mixture of isopropanol and hydrochloric acid may be used as solvent. The bases may be located on the paper as dark patches in ultraviolet light. The patches may be outlined in pencil, and then cut out with scissors. The base is extracted by warming the paper with dilute acid and its quantity determined by ultraviolet extinction at 260 mμ. The different bases are characterised by slightly different ultraviolet spectra. The base composition of RNA may also be determined by separating the nucleotides formed on alkaline hydrolysis by paper electrophoresis, or on columns, and determining their ultraviolet extinction. The base composition of DNA may also be determined from its buoyant density (see p. 130), or its melting temperature (see p. 158).

Table 2. *Base composition of some DNA's*

(Moles per 100 moles total bases)

Source	Adenine	Thymine	Guanine	Cytosine	$\dfrac{A+T}{G+C}$
M. lysodeikticus	13.1	14.2	33.0	39.6	0.38
E. coli	26.8	25.0	23.2	25.0	1.08
Wheat	27.3	27.1	22.7	22.8	1.20
Man	30.4	30.1	19.9	19.9	1.52
Sea urchin	31.6	31.6	18.0	19.2	1.70
Bacteriophage T$_2$	32.0	33.3	18.0	16.8*	1.88

*Hydroxymethylcytosine.

Table 2 shows the base compositions of some DNA's. (Values for 5-methylcytosine have been added to those of cytosine.) It is seen that although the DNA's differ in composition the number of moles of adenine and thymine are roughly equal, as are those of guanine and cytosine or 5-methylcytosine. This was first pointed out by E. Chargaff, who has collected 101 analyses of various DNA's and found the mean ratios of adenine to thymine and guanine to cytosine to be 1.009 and 1.001 respectively. These figures suggest that the true ratios are exactly one, and that deviations are due to analytical error. These ratios are explained by the conformation of DNA (see p. 154). It follows from these facts that DNA's can be characterised by their ratio of adenine + thymine:guanine + cytosine (the ratios of adenine *or* thymine:guanine *or* cytosine should, of course, be identical, but analytical errors will here be more marked).

In some RNA's, especially those of RNA viruses, the number of moles of adenine and uracil are roughly equal, as are those of guanine and cytosine. Thus, wound tumour virus has adenine, uracil, guanine, and cytosine in the molar proportions of 31.1, 31.3, 18.6, and 19.1 respectively. Most RNA's however, deviate from this equality; thus, the corresponding values for ribosomal RNA of *E. coli* are 25.2, 21.7, 31.5, and 21.6. Moreover, minor bases are found in many RNA's, such as alanine transfer RNA (see p. 146).

4. Structures of Nucleosides and Nucleotides

Further clues to the structures of nucleic acids come from those of the nucleotides, which are formed on their partial hydrolysis (see Figure 11). A nucleotide on complete hydrolysis yields one mole of a base, one mole of a sugar, and one mole of phosphoric acid. On enzymic dephosphorylation it yields one mole of phosphoric acid and one mole of a nucleoside. Figure 11 shows the structures of some nucleosides from nucleic acids. They all have a molecule of a base linked to C_1 of ribose or deoxyribose. The nucleotides are nucleosides with the 2', 3', or 5' hydroxyl esterified with phosphoric acid. (The carbon atoms of the sugar are numbered 1', 2', etc., to distinguish them from those of the bases.) The structure of one of the nucleotides derived from RNA, adenylic acid, is shown in Figure 11. Table 3 shows the names (and abbreviations) of the commonest bases, and of the nucleosides and 5'-nucleotides derived from them. All the nucleosides and nucleotides with deoxyribose have the prefix deoxy- except thymidine and thymidylic acid. This is because thymine riboside was thought not to occur naturally, although it has since been found in alanine transfer RNA (p. 146). Uracil is found attached to C_1 of ribose, either by its N_1 to give uridine or, less frequently, by its C_5 to give pseudouridine. Work at Cambridge around 1950, by A. R. Todd and his colleagues, completed previous evidence for the structures of the common nucleosides and nucleotides, and confirmed them by synthesis. Evidence for these structures is summarised below.

Adenosine: (1) Hydrolysis with dilute acid yields only D-ribose and adenine in equimolar amounts. Since the reducing properties of ribose are unmasked by the hydrolysis, C_1 of ribose must be linked to adenine.

(2) The ease of hydrolysis suggests that C_1 of ribose is linked to a nitrogen rather than a carbon atom of adenine. This nitrogen is not that of the amino group on C_6, since with nitrous acid adenosine gives a product which, on hydrolysis, yields hypoxanthine—the purine in which the 6-amino group of adenine is replaced by hydroxyl. Hence in adenosine this amino group was free to react with nitrous acid. Of the methylated adenines

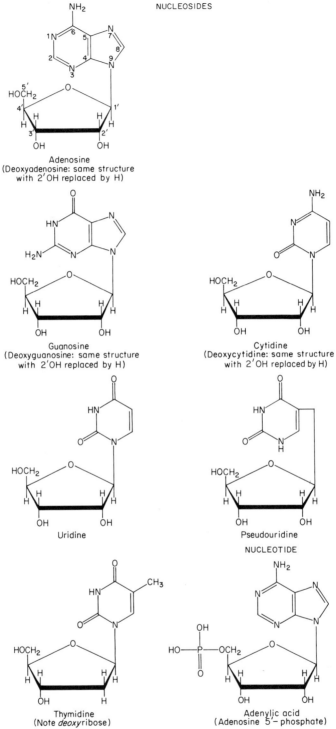

Figure 11. Some nucleosides and a nucleotide from nucleic acids.

136

Table 3. *Names of bases, nucleosides, and nucleotides of nucleic acids*

Base	Nucleoside	5′-Nucleotide
Adenine (A)	Adenosine	Adenosine 5′-monophosphate = Adenylic acid (AMP)
	Deoxyadenosine	Deoxyadenosine 5′-monophosphate = Deoxyadenylic acid (dAMP)
Guanine (G)	Guanosine	Guanosine 5′-monophosphate = Guanylic acid (GMP)
	Deoxyguanosine	Deoxyguanosine 5′-monophosphate = Deoxyguanylic acid (dGMP)
Cytosine (C)	Cytidine	Cytidine 5′-monophosphate = Cytidylic acid (CMP)
	Deoxycytidine	Deoxycytidine 5′-monophosphate = Deoxycytidylic acid (dCMP)
Uracil (U)	Uridine	Uridine 5′-monophosphate = Uridylic acid (UMP)
	Pseudouridine	Pseudouridine 5′-monophosphate = Pseudouridylic acid (ψUMP)
Thymine (T)	Thymidine	Thymidine 5′-monophosphate = Thymidylic acid (TMP)
Hypoxanthine	Inosine	Inosine 5′-monophosphate = Inosinic acid (IMP).

only the ultraviolet spectrum of 9-methyladenine resembles that of adenosine, suggesting that the link is to C_9.

(3) On oxidation, one mole of periodate is consumed per mole of adenosine to yield a dialdehyde but no formic acid (see p. 71). Hence the reaction is:

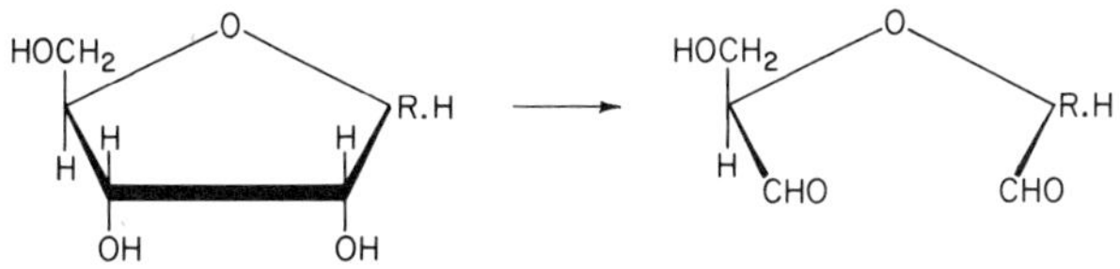

and not:

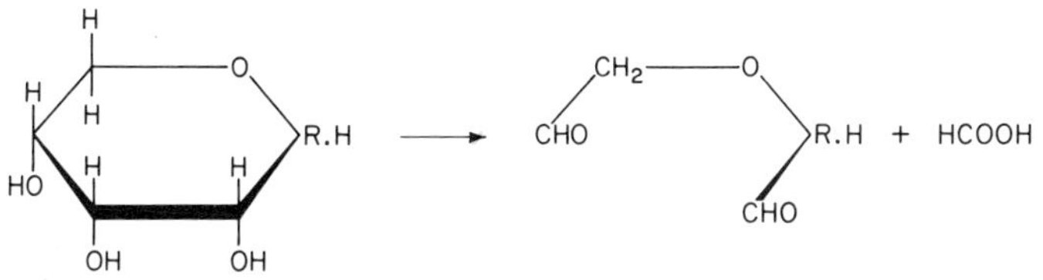

Hence ribose must have the furanose form. This is confirmed by the products of the methylation and hydrolysis of adenosine.

(4) That the glycosidic link has the β-configuration has been proved by the preparation of a cyclic derivative in which position 3 of adenine is linked to C_5 of ribose. This ring structure could not be formed if adenine was linked α to the ribose, since it would then be on the opposite side of the ribose ring from the 5'-hydroxyl. The structure of the cyclic derivative is:

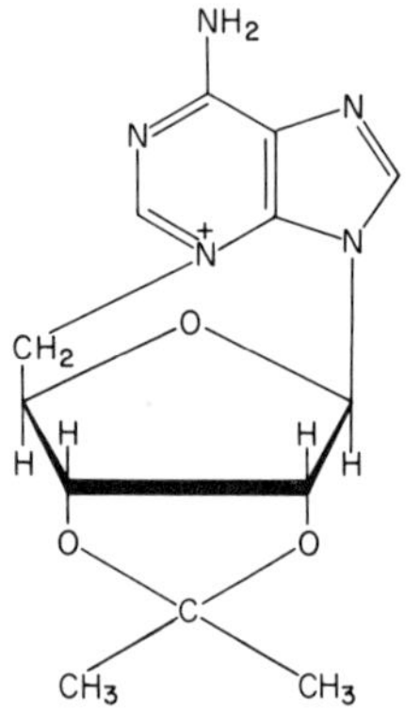

(5) The structure of adenosine has been confirmed by a number of syntheses, of which the following, a modification of the Fischer-Helferich method, is the best:

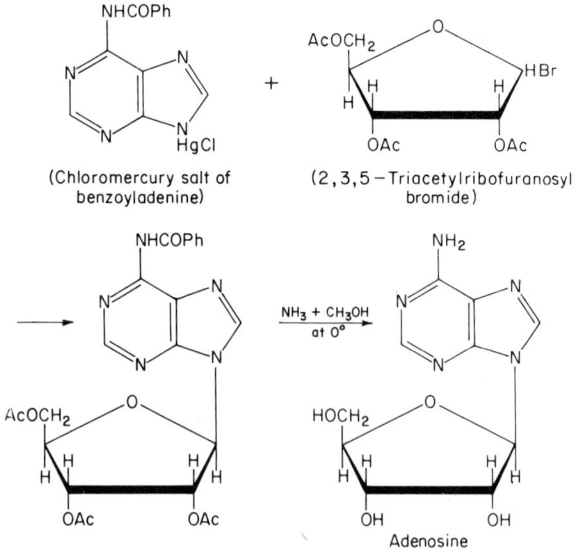

(Chloromercury salt of benzoyladenine)

(2,3,5 – Triacetylribofuranosyl bromide)

Adenosine

Guanosine. The structure has been proved in a similar way to that of adenosine and confirmed by a similar synthesis.

Uridine when methylated and hydrolysed gives ribose and 3-methyl-uracil, showing that N_1 and not N_3 forms the glycosidic link. The remaining points in the structure of uridine have been proved as for adenosine and confirmed by synthesis.

Cytidine. The structure is proved by its conversion to uridine by nitrous acid which replaces the amino group by hydroxyl. Its structure has been confirmed by synthesis.

Pseudouridine. Spectral evidence suggests that in pseudouridine ribose is attached to C_5 of uracil. This is confirmed by its degradation, by oxidation with periodate followed by reduction, to 5-hydroxymethyluracil:

The structure of pseudouridine has been conclusively proved by synthesis.

Deoxyadenosine and *deoxyguanosine* on hydrolysis with dilute acid yield adenine and guanine, respectively, together with 2-deoxy-D-ribose in equimolar amounts. *Deoxycytidine* and *thymidine* can only be hydrolysed with dilute acid if they are first reduced. They then yield 5,6-dihydro-cytosine and 5,6-dihydrothymine respectively and 2-deoxy-D-ribose in equimolar amounts. All four nucleosides react to a negligible extent with periodate showing that the deoxyribose has no adjacent hydroxyls, and hence must be furanose. That the glycosidic links are β and are to position 9 of the purines and 3 of the pyrimidines has been proved as for the ribonucleosides. The structures of all four have been confirmed by synthesis.

Adenosine 5′-phosphate (adenylic acid) on neutral hydrolysis yields adenosine, and on mild acid hydrolysis yields adenine and D-ribose-5-phosphate. These reactions prove the structure which has been confirmed by synthesis as follows: (see top of next page).

In this synthesis, which can be adapted for the synthesis of the other 5′-nucleotides, the 2′ and 3′ hydroxyls are protected before phosphorylation by the isopropylidene group, which is later removed by hydrolysis.

Guanosine, cytidine, and uridine 5′-phosphates. The structures of these have been proved similarly.

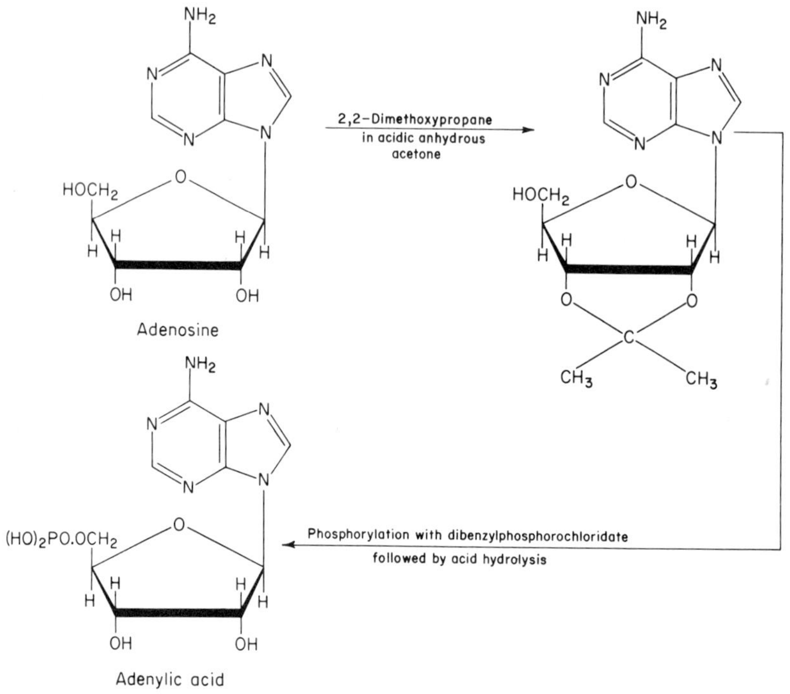

Adenosine

2,2-Dimethoxypropane in acidic anhydrous acetone →

Phosphorylation with dibenzylphosphorochloridate followed by acid hydrolysis ←

$(HO)_2PO.OCH_2$

Adenylic acid

Adenosine 2′-phosphate and *3′-phosphate* are both formed on alkaline hydrolysis of RNA (Figure 9). That their structures are:

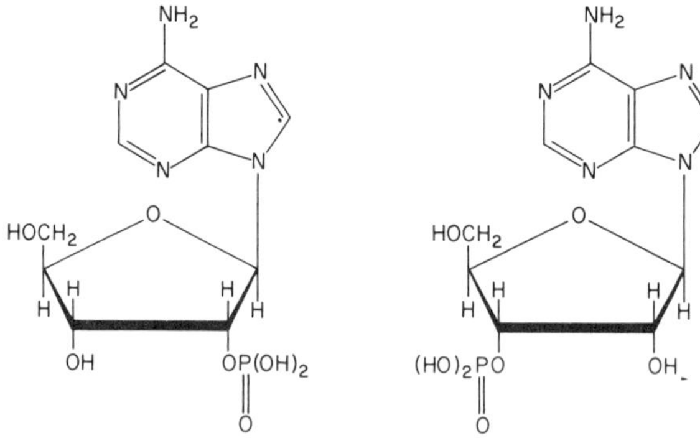

is proved as follows.

(1) The two isomers can be separated by ion-exchange chromatography. Hydrolysis of each gives adenosine and phosphoric acid.

(2) They are not oxidised by periodate showing that neither has *cis* hydroxyl groups.

(3) In dilute acid each of the phosphates is converted to a mixture of the two. This suggests that in each a free hydroxyl is adjacent to the phosphate group. Thus, glycerol-1-phosphate and glycerol-2-phosphate are interconverted in acid solution.

(4) Treatment of each with trifluoroacetic anhydride removes the elements of water to give the same secondary phosphate. This reaction can only be explained if this compound has the structure:

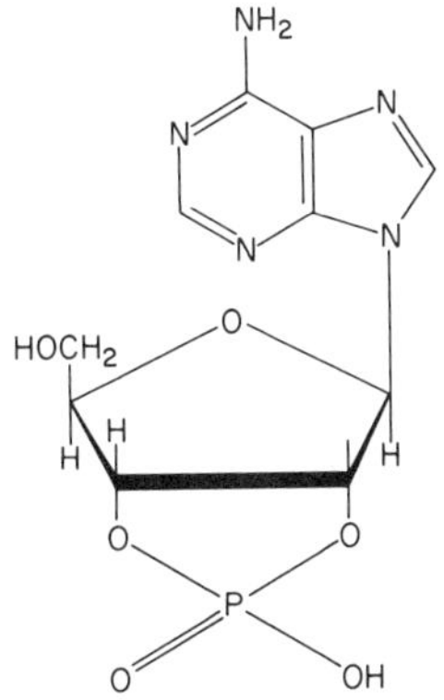

(5) The above reactions suggest that the compounds are adenosine-2′- and 3′-phosphates but do not distinguish one from the other. The two have been distinguished by identifying ribose-2- and 3-phosphates after brief acid hydrolysis, before appreciable phosphate migration has occurred. The ribose phosphates were identified by reduction to ribitol phosphates; ribitol 2-phosphate is dissymmetric and optically active, while the 3-phosphate is not:

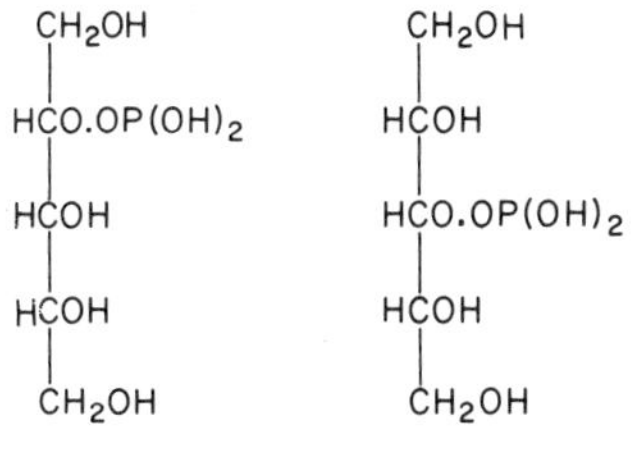

The structure of the two adenosine phosphates has been confirmed by other evidence, including X-ray diffraction and synthesis.

Guanosine, cytidine, and *uridine 2'- and 3'-phosphates* have been similarly identified.

The *5'-phosphates* of *deoxyadenosine, deoxyguanosine, deoxycytidine,* and *thymidine* are formed in good yield from DNA by enzymic hydrolysis (Figure 8). They can be separated on ion-exchange columns and they emerge in similar positions to the ribonucleoside 5'-phosphates rather than 3'-phosphates. This property, and their hydrolysis by enzymes specific for 5'-phosphates, indicates their structures which have been confirmed by synthesis. The *3'-phosphates* can also be obtained from DNA by enzymic hydrolysis (Figure 8), and can be isolated on ion-exchange columns. Their structures have been proved by synthesis.

5. Internucleotide Links in Nucleic Acids

The high molecular weights of DNA and RNA, and the formation of nucleotides on their hydrolysis, show that they are polynucleotides. Evidence which has proved how these nucleotides are linked together is summarised below. The linkages in RNA have been more difficult to prove than those in DNA since they could involve the 2'-hydroxyl as well as the 3'- and 5'-hydroxyls.

A. Internucleotide links in DNA

(1) Electrometric titrations of DNA show that each phosphorus atom has only one free hydroxyl.

(2) The 5'-phosphates of deoxyadenosine, deoxyguanosine, deoxycytidine, and thymidine can be isolated from enzymic hydrolysates of DNA in almost quantitative yield. Hence all, or almost all, internucleotide links must involve the 5'-hydroxyl of deoxyribose. The 3'-phosphates of the same nucleosides can also be isolated in good yields from hydrolysates with different enzymes. Hence, many internucleotide links must involve the 3' hydroxyl.

(3) The 3'-, 5'-diphosphates of deoxycytidine and thymidine can be isolated from acid hydrolysates of DNA, showing that both the 3' and 5' hydroxyls of at least some deoxyribose resides are involved in internucleotide links.

(4) Dinucleotides can be isolated from enzymic hydrolysates of DNA in which nuceotides are joined by $C_{3'}$—$C_{5'}$ links:

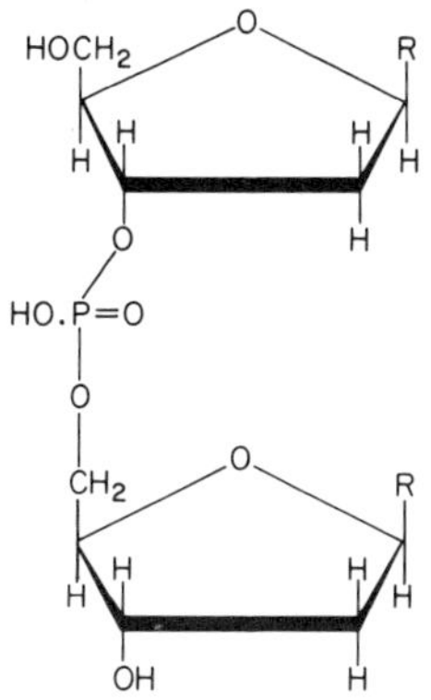

Dinucleotides with $C_{5'}$—$C_{5'}$ and $C_{3'}$—$C_{3'}$ links have not been found.
(5) This evidence is only consistent with the structure:

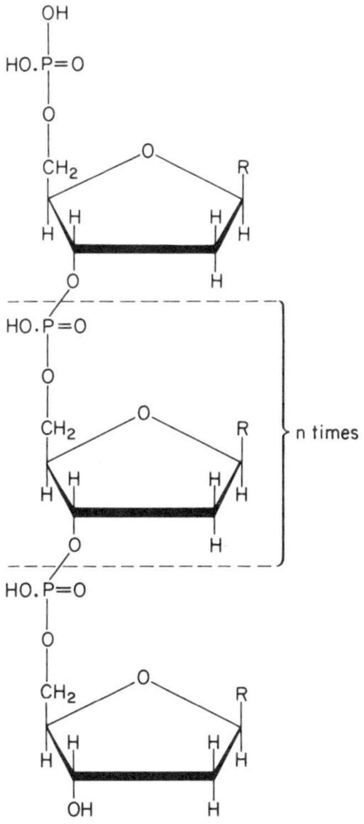

X-ray diffraction measurements of DNA agree with the above structure. Electron micrographs also suggest that DNA molecules are long and

unbranched. The two ends of the DNA molecule are distinguished by one (at the top in this drawing) having a 5'-hydroxyl and the other a 3'-hydroxyl, not involved in internucleotide links. The terminal 5'-hydroxyl has been shown here as phosphorylated, and the 3'-hydroxyl as free—a structure that is inferred from the fact that DNA is synthesised enzymically from nucleoside-5'-triphosphates.

B. Internucleotide links in RNA

(1) Electrometric titrations again show only secondary phosphoryl dissociations.

(2) Hydrolysis of RNA with a phosphodiesterase from snake venom yields the 5'-phosphates of adenosine, guanosine, cytidine and uridine in up to 60% yield. Hence, many internucleotide links must involve the 5'-hydroxyl.

(3) Unlike DNA, RNA is completely hydrolysed by warm dilute alkali. It gives a mixture of the 2'- and 3'-phosphates of the component nucleosides in quantitative yield. At first sight this might suggest that both the 2'- and 3'-hydroxyls are involved in internucleotide links. However, experiments with synthetic phosphates make it clear that the reason why RNA is labile to alkali must be because there is a free hydroxyl (on $C_{2'}$ or $C_{3'}$) adjacent to an internucleotide link (on $C_{3'}$ or $C_{2'}$); and that migration of the phosphate group to the adjacent hydroxyl will certainly occur during hydrolysis. Thus dimethyl phosphate:

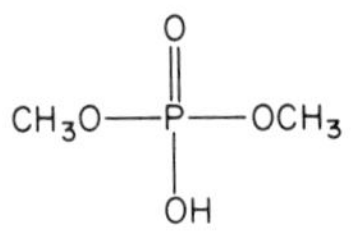

$$
\underset{\underset{\displaystyle OH}{|}}{CH_3O—\overset{\overset{\displaystyle O}{\|}}{P}—OCH_3}
$$

like DNA, is stable to alkali. But glycerol-1-methylphosphate is readily hydrolysed to methanol and a mixture of glycerol 1- and 2-phosphates:

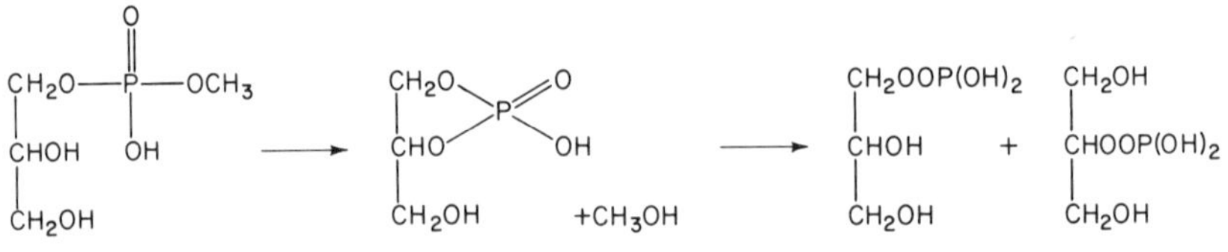

It has been proved that the cyclic phosphate shown is an intermediate, and also that nucleoside cyclic 2',3'-phosphates are intermediates in the hydrolysis of RNA by alkali.

It may therefore be concluded that every internucleotide link of RNA involves either the 2'- or the 3'-hydroxyl.

(4) Pancreatic ribonuclease will partially hydrolyse RNA liberating oligonucleotides and free pyrimidine nucleoside 3'-phosphates. Since migration of phosphate can occur it cannot be concluded that the 3'- rather than the 2'-hydroxyl is involved in internucleotide links. However, the enzyme has been found to remove the benzyl group from cytidine and uridine 3'-benzyl phosphates:

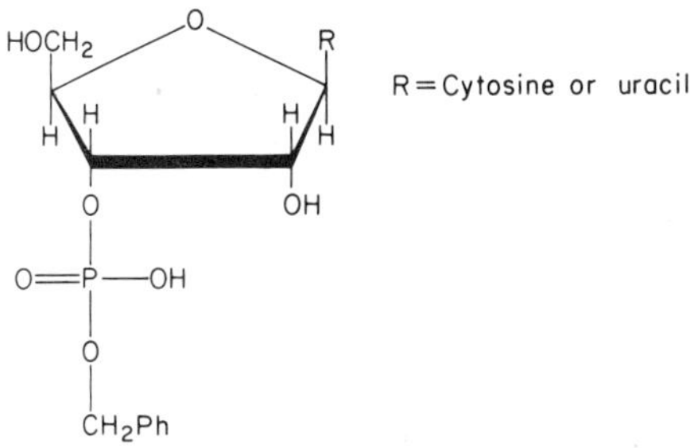

$R = $ Cytosine or uracil

It will not hydrolyse the 2'- or 5'-benzyl phosphates, nor any of the purine nucleoside benzyl phosphates. The enzyme is clearly specific for pyrimidine nucleoside 3'-phosphodiesters. Another ribonuclease from spleen will partially hydrolyse RNA liberating free purine nucleoside 3'-phosphates. It will hydrolyse adenosine 3'-benzyl phosphate but not the 2'-phosphate. It is clear that internucleotide links of RNA must involve the 3'- rather than the 2'-hydroxyl.

It follows that the structure of RNA may be represented in the same way as that of DNA above, but with the replacement of deoxyribose by ribose. Alanine transfer RNA (see p. 146) and certain other RNA's have been proved to have a terminal 5'-phosphate and no terminal 3'-phosphate, as shown in this structure. X-ray diffraction measurements agree with this structure, and electron micrographs, particularly of tobacco mosaic virus RNA, confirm that the molecules are unbranched.

Complete structural formulae of polynucleotides are tedious to draw, and abbreviations have been introduced. One system would represent the above structures of DNA or RNA as:

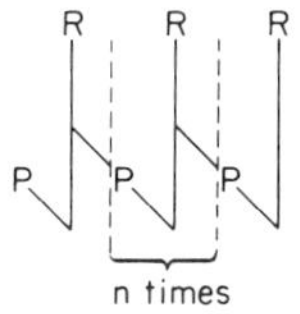

n times

The vertical lines represent sugar residues, while the diagonal lines represent bonds from $C_{3'}$ and $C_{5'}$. Ribose and deoxyribose are not distinguished but bases may be represented by their initial letters. Thus a particular trinucleotide could be represented:

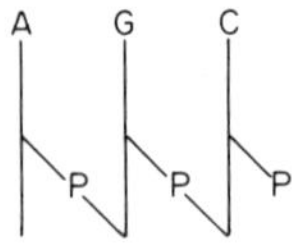

The adenosine or deoxyadenosine residue is shown here with a terminal 5'-hydroxyl, and the cytidine or deoxycytidine with a terminal 3'-phosphate.

Another system of abbreviations represents the polynucleotide chain by a series of letters. A ribonucleoside is represented by the initial letter of its base, and a deoxyribonucleoside by the same initial letter with d before it. The letter p on the left of one of these symbols represents the 5'-phosphate, and on the right the 3'-phosphate. Thus, the above trinucleotide would be represented ApGpCp or dApdGpdCp.

6. The Covalent Structure of Alanine Transfer RNA of Yeast and 5s RNA of E. Coli

The remaining step in determining the covalent structure of a nucleic acid is to find the number of residues of each kind of nucleotide, and their arrangement, in the molecule. Complete covalent structures have only been determined for a few RNA's of low molecular weight. In this section methods used for determining nucleotide sequences in RNA will be illustrated by describing first the determination of the covalent structure of alanine transfer RNA by R. W. Holley and his colleagues at Cornell University around 1964. Methods for investigating nucleotide sequences in DNA will be summarised in the next section. Living cells contain somewhat more than twenty kinds of transfer RNA, each of which forms an intermediate compound with one kind of amino acid during the synthesis of proteins. They have molecular weights around 25,000 and contain around eighty nucleotides.

A. Isolation of pure alanine transfer RNA

Preliminary experiments showed that pure alanine transfer RNA could be isolated by countercurrent distribution between a phosphate buffer, and formamide in isopropanol. A large apparatus was then built which could fractionate the combined transfer RNA from 100-lb lots of baker's yeast with a yield of around 350 mg of alanine transfer RNA.

B. Determination of nucleotide composition

It was seen in the last chapter that an amino acid analysis of a protein, together with a molecular weight determination, will often allow the exact number of amino acid residues per molecule to be calculated. Nucleotide analyses are less useful in giving a first clue to the structure of nucleic acids. This is partly because only four nucleotides predominate and therefore very precise analyses would be required to determine the exact number per molecule of molecular weight 25,000. In addition, a number of minor nucleotides with unusual purines or pyrimidines also occur, and routine methods have not yet been worked out for their quantitative determination in hydrolysates of nucleic acids.

Preliminary analyses by column chromatography suggested that alkaline hydrolysates of alanine transfer RNA contained 11 residues of adenylic, 29 of guanylic, 25 of cytidylic, 17 of uridylic and 3 of pseudo-uridylic acid per molecule. Later work showed that these figures were not very accurate, and that a number of minor nucleotides had been missed.

C. Enzymic digestion

In determining the amino acid sequence of a protein it is nowadays normal to first digest with an enzyme, such as trypsin, and determine sequences in the peptides which are formed. The protein is then digested with a different enzyme to give peptides which overlap parts of those previously obtained. The sequence in the protein can then be deduced from those in the two sets of peptides. A similar principle was used in determining the nucleotide sequence of this RNA, the two enzymes used being pancreatic ribonuclease and takadiastase ribonuclease T_1.

Pancreatic ribonuclease severs RNA molecules between the 3'-phosphate of a pyrimidine nucleotide and the 5'-hydroxyl of the adjoining nucleotide (see Figure 9, p. 132). The alanine transfer RNA was hydrolysed at pH 7.0 for fourteen hours at 37° with this enzyme. Ribonuclease T_1 severs RNA molecules between the 3'-phosphate of guanylic or inosinic acids, and the 5'-hydroxyl of the adjoining nucleotide (Figure 9). The transfer RNA was hydrolysed at pH 7.5 and 37° for twenty-four hours with this enzyme. It was also found that the RNA could be severed into fewer larger fragments by digestion with this enzyme at pH 7.5 and 0°.

The oligonucleotides from these digestions were separated by chromatography on columns of DEAE-Sephadex and DEAE-cellulose, sometimes followed by paper electrophoresis. A sample of each oligonucleotide was then hydrolysed with alkali to its component nucleoside 3'-phosphates, which were separated by two-dimensional paper chromatography and identified. This involved proving the structures of a number of purines and pyrimidines not previously found in RNA. Summation of the nucleotides isolated from the digested RNA showed that the original molecule contained seventy-seven nucleotides including nine with minor bases.

D. Base sequences of oligonucleotides

The complete digests with pancreatic ribonuclease and ribonuclease T_1 gave fragments containing from one to eight nucleotides. The products of alkaline hydrolysis immediately proved the sequences of all dinucleotides. For example if a dinucleotide from the pancreatic ribonuclease digest yielded guanosine 3'-phosphate and cytidine 3'-phosphate, the sequence must have been GpCp since this ribonuclease always leaves a pyrimidine nucleoside 3'-phosphate at the end of the chain. Conversely if a nucleotide from the T_1 digest yielded Gp and Cp then its sequence must have been CpGp.

The sequences of some of the larger fragments were also immediately clear from their hydrolysis products. For example an oligonucleotide from the pancreatic ribonuclease digest yielded 2 Gp and 1 Tp; its sequence was therefore GpGpTp. If the sequence of a fragment was not clear from its hydrolysis products, it was severed with the enzyme not used in its preparation into smaller fragments; from their sequences that of the parent fragment could usually be deduced. For example a fragment from the pancreatic ribonuclease digest yielded 2 Gp, 1 Ap, and 1 Cp on alkaline hydrolysis. The pyrimidine Cp must have been terminal. Digestion with ribonuclease T_1 yielded 2 Gp and a fragment yielding 1 Ap and 1 Cp on hydrolysis. Therefore the original sequence was GpGpApCp.

For the determination of sequences in the larger oligonucleotides a method was devised which used snake venom phosphodiesterase. This is specific for terminal nucleosides with free 3'-hydroxyls, and it removes them as 5'-phosphates (see Figure 9, p. 132). If incubated with an oligonucleotide with its terminal 3'-hydroxyl free, it will yield a mixture of smaller oligonucleotides formed by successive removal of the terminal nucleotide. Merely from the products of alkaline hydrolysis of each of these fragments it is possible to deduce the original sequence. For example, an octanucleotide from the pancreatic ribonuclease digest yielded 2 Ap, 5 Gp, and 1 Up on alkaline hydrolysis; the pyrimidine nucleotide Up must have been terminal. The octanucleotide was incubated with alkaline phosphatase to remove the terminal 3'-phosphate, and then incubated with snake venom diesterase. The resulting fragments of different length were separated on a column of DEAE-cellulose. Each of these on hydrolysis with alkali yielded a nucleoside from the terminus together with nucleotides, and these were separated by paper chromatography. Fragments were found which contained 7, 6, 5, and 4 residues; the terminal nucleoside yielded by each of these was G, A, G, and A respectively. Hence the sequence of the original octanucleotide must have been GpGpGpApGp ApGpUp.

Figure 12 shows the complete covalent structure of alanine transfer RNA that was deduced by piecing together the sequences of the many

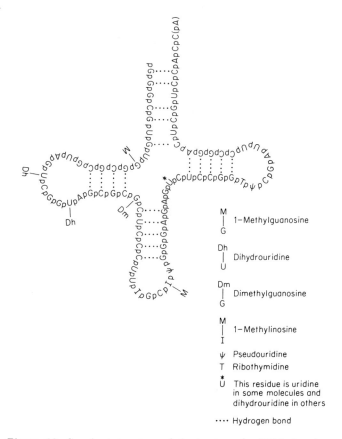

Figure 12. Covalent structure of alanine transfer RNA showing possible folding established by hydrogen bonds between pairs of bases. The terminal adenylic acid residene, shown in parentheses, was absent from the sample whose structure was determined but is essential for biological activity.

fragments. (The chain is shown in a possible folded structure stabilised by hydrogen bonds between pairs of bases, see p. 157). The molecule had a terminal 5'-phosphate, rather than 5'-hydroxyl and a terminal 3'-hydroxyl, rather than 3'-phosphate. These points were proved by two fragments in the pancreatic ribonuclease digest. Most of these fragments have a terminal 5'-hydroxyl at one end and terminal 3'-phosphate at the other. But one fragment (pGpGpGpCp) had a terminal 5'-phosphate, and another (C) a terminal 3'-hydroxyl, and they were clearly derived from the two ends of the molecule. It has however been shown that the biologically active RNA has an additional adenylic acid residue attached to the terminal 3'-hydroxyl (shown in parentheses in Figure 12) which was lost during the isolation of the RNA used for analysis.

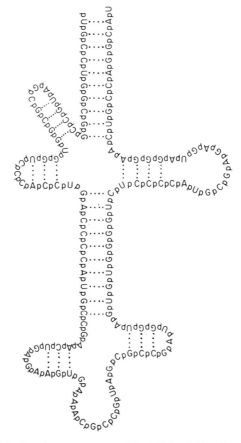

Figure 13. Covalent structure of 5s RNA of *E. coli* with base pairing as suggested by H. Boedtker and D. E. Kelling.

F. Sanger and colleagues have more recently determined the complete covalent structure of 5s RNA of *E. coli* (Figure 13). This is a small component of ribosomal RNA which contains 120 nucleotides with adenine, guanine, cytosine, and uracil as the only bases. Their approach differed from that on alanine transfer RNA in some important respects. The RNA was isolated from bacteria which were uniformly labelled with [32]P. The nucleotides in each enzymic digest of RNA were fractionated by electrophoresis, first on a sheet of cellulose acetate paper and then on a sheet of DEAE-cellulose paper. The nucleotides were located by autoradiography and their phosphorus contents determined by radioactive counting. After elution, oligonucleotides were submitted to further digestion and fractionation. Fractionation on paper is more rapid and efficient than on columns, and assay of nucleotides by radioactivity is so sensitive that only a few milligrammes of RNA are needed.

7. Nucleotide Sequences in DNA

The molecular weights of all DNA's are so great that it is at present inconceivable that the complete nucleotide sequence in any could be determined. Methods have however been developed by which some facts about base sequences in DNA can be obtained; the most important are summarised below.

A. Nearest neighbour frequencies

Since there are four common nucleotides in DNA there are sixteen possible dinucleotide sequences, or "nearest neighbour pairs", namely: ApA, ApT, ApG, ApC, TpA, TpT, TpG, TpC, GpA, GpT, GpG, GpC, CpA, CpT, CpG, CpC. If a DNA sample contained equimolar amounts of all four nucleotides, and they were arranged at random in the chains, then each of these dinucleotide sequences would form $\frac{100}{16} = 6.25\%$, or the fraction 0.0625, of all the dinucleotide sequences which occur from the 5'-phosphate end of the molecule to the 3'-hydroxyl end. (In the chain pGpCpC-pApTpA, for example, such dinucleotide sequences are GpC, CpC, CpA, ApT, and TpA.) A. Kornberg and his colleagues have devised a method by which the actual frequencies can be determined.

Their method uses the enzyme DNA polymerase, that catalyses the condensation of the four deoxyribonucleoside 5'-triphosphates to form DNA, with the elimination of pyrophosphate. The reaction only occurs in the presence of DNA. This DNA acts as a template, and the DNA that is formed is an exact copy of it both in base composition and sequence. In nearest neighbour determinations, DNA is synthesised with one of the 5'-triphosphates labelled with ^{32}P in the α-phosphoric acid residue. This residue becomes linked to the 3'-hydroxyl of neighbouring nucleotides in the DNA that is synthesised. This labelled DNA is then enzymically hydrolysed to the 3'-phosphates of the component nucleosides. The original bond from the ^{32}P to the 5'-hydroxyl of the parent nucleoside is thus severed, and it is left attached to the 3'-hydroxyls of the nearest neighbours. The ^{32}P contents of each of the four 3'-phosphates are measured, and these are proportional to the frequencies with which they occurred next to the nucleotide that was labelled.

An example of a determination by Kornberg and colleagues of nearest neighbour frequencies in the DNA from *Mycobacterium phlei* should make the method clearer. This DNA was first used as template for DNA synthesis with (^{32}P)dATP. The DNA formed was hydrolysed, and the four nucleoside 3'-phosphates separated by paper electrophoresis. Thymidine phosphate gave 873 counts per minute in the particular radio-active counter used; deoxyadenosine phosphate gave 1710; deoxycytidine phosphate gave 4430; and deoxyguanosine phosphate gave 4690. These counts expressed as fractions of one are 0.075, 0.146, 0.378, and 0.401 respectively. Hence, of all four sequences of the type *X*pA along the chains of this DNA, 7.5% are TpA, 14.6% are ApA, 37.8% are CpA, and

Table 4. *Nearest neighbour frequencies in M. phlei DNA*

Reaction with (^{32}P)dATP			Reaction with (^{32}P)TTP		
Sequence	Fraction of		Sequence	Fraction of	
	*X*pA sequences	*X*pX sequences		*X*pT sequences	*X*pX sequences
TpA	0.075	0.012	TpT	0.157	0.025
ApA	0.146	0.024	ApT	0.194	0.031
CpA	0.378	0.062	CpT	0.279	0.045
GpA	0.401	0.066	GpT	0.370	0.060
Reaction with (^{32}P)dGTP			Reaction with (^{32}P)dCTP		
Sequence	Fraction of		Sequence	Fraction of	
	*X*pG sequences	*X*pX sequences		*X*pC sequences	*X*pX sequences
TpG	0.187	0.063	TpC	0.182	0.061
ApG	0.134	0.045	ApC	0.189	0.064
CpG	0.414	0.139	CpC	0.268	0.090
GpG	0.265	0.089	GpC	0.361	0.122

40.1% are GpA. Similar experiments with (^{32}P)dCTP, (^{32}P)dGTP, and (^{32}P)TTP gave three more sets of four frequencies shown in Table 4. To determine the fraction which each dinucleotide sequence forms of the possible sixteen, each of the four sequences XpA must be multiplied by the fraction which adenine molecules form of the total base molecules of the DNA; and each of the four sequences XpC, XpG, and XpT must similarly be multiplied by the molar fractions of cytosine, guanine, and thymine, respectively. These fractions can either be determined by direct analysis of the DNA, or calculated from the relative incorporation of the four labelled nucleotides. For *M. phlei* DNA the values were determined as adenine, 0.164; thymine, 0.162; guanine, 0.337; cytosine, 0.337. The results of these multiplications are shown in Table 4, and give the fractions which each of the sixteen dinucleotide sequences forms of the total in this DNA. For example, the sequence TpA forms the fraction 0.012, or 12%, of the total.

Nearest neighbour frequencies show that the nucleotides in this and other DNA's are not arranged at random. DNA always contains equimolar amounts of adenine and thymine, and of guanine and cytosine (see p. 134). It follows that if the nucleotides of DNA were arranged randomly along the chains the sequences ApA, ApT, TpA, and TpT would have equal frequencies, as would the sequences GpG, GpC, CpG, and CpC. Table 4 shows that these frequencies are not equal. An exception is d(A—T) copolymer which is formed when DNA polymerase acts on TTP and dATP without any primer. The frequencies of its four possible dinucleotide sequences are ApT, 0.5; TpA, 0.5; ApA, 0; TpT, 0. It may be concluded that A and T alternate along the molecules. Nearest neighbour frequencies also confirm the Watson and Crick conformation of DNA as discussed later (p. 154).

B. Diphenylamine degradation

The internucleotide linkages of DNA are more stable than those of RNA, and on mild acid hydrolysis the chain of deoxyribose residues remains intact. However, the glycosidic linkages to all purines, but not pyrimidines, are hydrolysed to give a product known as apurinic acid. The hydrolysis is best done in 66% formic acid at 30°. If, however, the formic acid contains 2% diphenylamine all the deoxyribose residues that originally had purines attached are removed. Phosphate groups linking two such residues are liberated as inorganic phosphate. Phosphate groups linking one of these residues to a pyrimidine nucleotide remain attached to that nucleotide. Hence, pyrimidine nucleotides which originally lay between two purine nucleotides are released as nucleoside 3', 5'-diphosphates. Clusters of two or more pyrimidine nucleosides are released as di- and oligonucleotides with terminal phosphate groups at both ends. The following illustrates the severing of a hypothetical DNA chain:

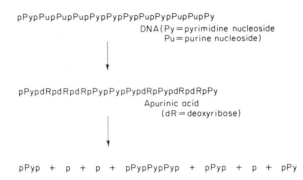

pPypPupPupPupPypPypPypPupPypPupPupPy
DNA(Py=pyrimidine nucleoside
Pu=purine nucleoside)

pPypdRpdRpdRpPypPypPypdRpPypdRpdRpPy
Apurinic acid
(dR=deoxyribose)

pPyp + p + p + pPypPypPyp + pPyp + p + pPy

K. Burton and colleagues have used this reaction extensively to obtain information about the frequencies with which different nucleotide sequences occur in DNA. The proportion of purine nucleotide phosphorus in the original DNA that is released as inorganic phosphate gives the frequency with which purine nucleotides occur in clusters of two or more. Also the pyrimidine oligonucleotides can be separated by paper chromatography and their structures determined.

8. Conformations of Nucleic Acids

The biological properties of nucleic acids, like those of proteins, depend on their molecules being arranged in specific conformations (see p. 12). The self-copying of living cells is founded on the conformation of DNA discovered by J. D. Watson and F. H. C. Crick. Less is known about RNA conformations, but the biological properties of transfer RNA's, at least, are founded on their conformations.

A. Conformation of DNA

In 1952 Watson and Crick deduced the conformation in which DNA molecules are found in nature. X-ray diffraction, and other physical measurements, had suggested that DNA molecules occur in long helixes, each helix being formed from two or more molecules bound side by side by hydrogen bonds. Titrations suggested that the phosphoric acid groups of these bonded molecules are on the outside of the helix. Analyses also showed that in every sample of DNA the number of residues of adenine and thymine are always equal, as are those of guanine and cytosine (see p. 134).

With these facts as a guide, Watson and Crick managed to deduce the natural conformation of DNA, largely by inspired arranging of models of DNA molecules together until a regular helix was obtained. They suggested that each helix is right-handed and is formed from a pair of DNA molecules of equal length aligned side by side in opposite directions —that is, the free 3'-hydroxyl at the end of one molecule is adjacent to the free 5'-phosphate at the end of its partner. (The helix itself is sometimes called the DNA molecule, and is then said to be composed of two DNA "strands".) Figure 14 illustrates the manner in which, they suggested, the paired molecules are bound. Wherever adenine occurs in one molecule it

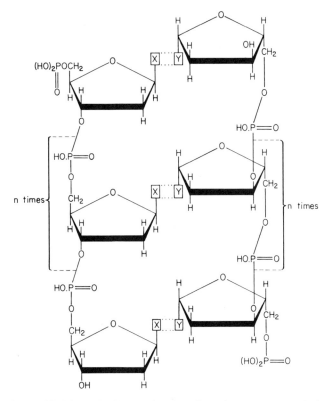

Figure 14. Two DNA molecules bound as suggested by Watson and Crick. X and Y represent bases linked by hydrogen bonds. When X is adenine, Y is thymine, and vice versa; when X is guanine, Y is cytosine, and vice versa.

is hydrogen bonded to thymine in the adjacent molecule, and wherever guanine occurs it is hydrogen bonded to cytosine. (The ratio $\frac{A+T}{G+C}$ is therefore the same in each molecule.) As a result, although any sequence of nucleotides can occur, the sequence in one molecule determines that in the other. This was a fact of extreme biological interest. It suggested that a DNA helix in the chromosomes of a living cell might direct the formation of copies of itself by its paired molecules separating, and each directing the formation of a new partner of the correct sequence. It thus became clear

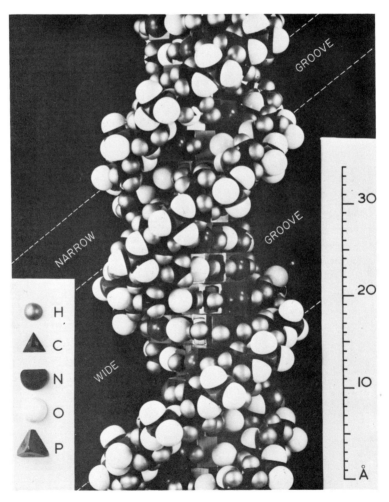

Figure 15. A model of a DNA double helix. (By kind permission of Professor M. H. F. Wilkins.)

for the first time how the self-copying of living organisms could be founded on organic chemistry.

The conformation of DNA has since been investigated in detail by M. H. F. Wilkins and colleagues by X-ray diffraction, and it is clear that in nature DNA has essentially the conformation proposed by Watson and Crick. (The only known exception is the DNA of the bacteriophage ϕX 174 which consists of single, unpaired, molecules.) The conformation of DNA varies slightly with the humidity. That of the "B" form in which DNA occurs in nature is shown in Figures 15.

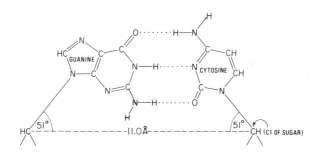

Figure 16. Adenine and thymine, and guanine and cytosine as hydrogen bonded in DNA.

Figure 16 shows details of the hydrogen bonding between bases. This is reinforced by hydrophobic attractions between the bases, and consequently the structure of DNA is fairly stable to agents that weaken hydrogen bonds. It is seen that in each of the nucleotide pairs the distance between C_1 of the two sugars is the same (11.0 Å). Also, the angle between the bond linking C_1 of each sugar to its base, and the line joining adjacent C_1's, is the same (51°) for all four nucleotides. These facts mean that each sugar and phosphate residue is arranged in the same position relative to the axis of the helix no matter to which nucleotide it belongs. The helix has therefore the same dimensions throughout its length. Only consistent pairing between adenine and thymine, and guanine and cytosine, can give this regular, and hence very stable, structure.

The bases, sugars and phosphate groups all recur at intervals of 3.4 Å along the helix axis. One turn of the helix contains ten paired nucleotides and hence recurs every 34 Å (Figure 15). The diameter of the helix is about 20 Å. The bases lie with the planes of their rings roughly perpendicular to the helix axis, while the planes of the sugar rings are roughly in line with it. A narrow and a wide helical groove run the length of the structure. The narrow groove is the space between the paired molecules; the wide groove is the space between successive turns when the pair is wound into a helix (Figure 15). In DNA which contains 5-hydroxymethyl-cytosine (see p. 133), some of the hydroxymethyl groups are linked glycosidically to glucose, and these glucose residues lie in the wide groove. In nuclei of higher organisms DNA is bound to basic proteins, named protamines and histones, by ionic bonds between the negative phosphate groups of DNA and the positive arginine and lysine side chains of the proteins. It is believed that these protein chains are coiled around the DNA helix in the wide or narrow groove.

That DNA molecules occur in pairs of equal length aligned in opposite directions, with adenine paired with thymine and guanine with cytosine is confirmed by nearest neighbour frequencies in DNA (see p. 151). The following frequencies should always be equal: ApA and TpT; CpA and TpG; GpA and TpC; CpT and ApG; GpT and ApC; GpG and CpC. Table 4 (p. 152) shows that for *M. phlei* DNA they are.

When DNA in solution is heated to around 80° or subjected to extremes of pH or to certain reagents, it is denatured: the helix collapses and the paired molecules wholly or partly separate and form random coils. The denaturation of a solution of DNA is characterised by a rise of about 40% in its extinction coefficient in ultraviolet light, known as the "hyperchromic effect." The middle of the temperature range over which the rise occurs is known as the "melting temperature" (T_m) and, in solutions of defined pH and salt concentration, it is characteristic of each nucleic acid. It may be determined in a spectrophotometer whose cells can be heated to known temperatures. T_m is low for d(A—T) copolymer which has alternating residues of adenine and thymine along each of the molecules of the double helix, and high for (dG):(dC) copolymer which has guanine in one of the paired molecules and cytosine in the other. (Both of these polymers can be prepared with the enzyme DNA polymerase.) The T_m's of most other DNA's lie between these two, and are higher the greater their content of guanine plus cytosine which can in fact be determined from the T_m. The greater stability of the guanine-cytosine pair has been attributed to its having three hydrogen bonds rather than two (Figure 19), but it appears that hydrophobic attractions are also greater between guanine and cytosine than between adenine and thymine. Each individual molecule in a DNA sample denatures suddenly as its T_m is reached, but the temperature range over which denaturation of a sample of DNA occurs can be wide because the sample can contain molecules of widely different composition.

Denaturation of DNA samples in which differences in composition between molecules are not great, such as those from viruses and bacteria, can often be reversed. The denatured DNA, in a solution of high ionic strength, is held at about 25° below T_m. The helixes become re-formed, and the DNA regains all its properties including its biological ones. If this renaturation is carried out in the presence of RNA of the same base sequence as one or both strands of the DNA, DNA:RNA hybrid double helixes are formed.

B. Conformation of RNA

Molecular models show that RNA, like DNA, could exist in double helixes with guanine bonded to cytosine, and adenine bonded to uracil rather than thymine. Moreover, when equimolar amounts of poly-adenylic acid and polyuridylic acid in dilute solution are mixed, the ultra-violet extinction of the solution falls, and a complex containing adenine and uracil in equimolar amounts can be isolated. Its properties resemble those of native DNA. X-ray diffraction shows it to have a helical structure with almost the same dimensions as DNA, and in solution in neutral 0.15 M sodium chloride its T_m is 60°.

However, most samples of RNA do not contain equimolar amounts of adenine and uracil, and of guanine and cytosine. Hence separate molecules of equal length cannot be base paired throughout their length as in DNA. Solutions of RNA have lower viscosities than those of DNA of similar molecular weight, showing that the molecules are less elongated. X-ray diffraction and optical rotation measurements do, however, suggest that regions of most RNA molecules are helical. Also, most RNA's show a hyperchromic effect of a size that suggests that about half of their bases are paired. Denaturation is readily reversible suggesting that the regions of base pairing are short. It is therefore probable that most RNA molecules are folded back on themselves and the folds secured by hydrogen bonds.

It is possible to arrange each of the known base sequences of transfer RNA's into a number of conformations of this type. Figure 14 shows one of these for alanine transfer RNA. The sequence I—G—C is exposed on one loop, and is believed to be the "anticodon" which hydrogen bonds the transfer RNA to the correct "codon" of three nucleotides in messenger

RNA during protein synthesis. The sequence G—T—ψ—C—G is exposed on another loop. This sequence is also found in other transfer RNA's and may bind the RNA to ribosomes. Other transfer RNA's can also be arranged in folded conformations in which this sequence, and the anticodon, are exposed on adjacent loops.

FURTHER READING

1. M. Florkin and E. H. Stotz, editors, *Comprehensive Biochemistry*, Elsevier Publishing Co., Amsterdam, 1962–1965, vol. 8.

2. T. L. V. Ulbricht, *Introduction to Nucleic Acids*, Oldbourne Press, London, 1965.

3. R. W. Holley, J. Apgar, G. A. Everett, J. T. Madison, M. Marquisee, S. H. Merrill, J. R. Penswick, and A. Zamir, *Structure of a Ribonucleic Acid*, Science, **147** (1965) 1462. Description of the elucidation of the structure of alanine transfer RNA by the workers themselves.

Chapter 6

Lipids and Miscellaneous Compounds

1. Isolation and Fractionation of Lipids

Lipids are sometimes defined as that group of compounds which may be extracted from living organisms with nonpolar solvents such as ether, acetone, chloroform, and benzene. However, by this definition lipids include many compounds that are unrelated in structure and function and, since the difference between "solubility" and "insolubility" in these solvents cannot be clearly defined, the borderline between lipids and non-lipids is left unclear. It is becoming usual to define lipids as long-chain fatty acids and their derivatives, and that will be done here. Lipids may then be subdivided into simple lipids (fatty acids and their esters) and complex lipids (fatty-acid esters that have other residues attached, such as choline phosphate).

A. Isolation of lipids from natural sources

A large part of the lipids in a living organism are bonded to proteins by noncovalent forces which involve water molecules. If the water is removed these bonds are broken. Hence solvents used for extracting lipids usually include ethanol, methanol, or acetone, which act as dehydrating agents,

161

together with ether, petroleum ether, or chloroform. A mixture of ethanol and ether is the commonest solvent, and extractions are usually done at room temperature. At lower temperatures lipids are not soluble enough for good extraction, while at higher temperatures lipase enzymes become active and also chemical degradation can occur.

After extraction, the solvents are removed by vacuum evaporation, and lipids are extracted from the aqueous residue with ether, petroleum ether, or chloroform which are in turn removed *in vacuo*. The lipid residue usually contains nonlipid contaminants such as sugars, amino acids, and inorganic ions which may be removed by washing with water.

B. Fractionation with solvents

Phospholipids are less soluble in acetone than other lipids and can often be precipitated from lipid mixtures by adding acetone. The conditions must be adjusted with each lipid mixture to ensure maximum precipitation of phospholipids and minimum precipitation of other lipids.

Phospholipids can also be separated from each other on account of their varying solubilities in organic solvents. Thus if the mixed phospholipids of the yolks of hens' eggs are dissolved in ethanol and cooled to $-35°$ most of the phospholipids precipitate except lecithin. Again, phosphatidyl serine and phosphatidyl ethanolamine can be separated from the inositol phospholipids of brain by their solubility in a mixture of 1 volume of chloroform to 1.45 volumes of methanol.

C. Fractionation by chromatography on columns

The most useful columns are those of silicic acid, which is sometimes mixed with the inert powder celite to increase the rate of flow. Phospholipids can readily be separated from other lipids by first eluting these from the column with chloroform or ether, and then eluting the phospholipids with ethanol. More subtle variations of solvents will give more refined fractionation. Thus, successive elution of total lipids with different mixtures of hexane, benzene, ether, and methanol gives sterol esters, triglycerides plus free fatty acids, free sterols, diglycerides, monoglycerides, and phospholipids in successive fractions. Lipid fractions can also be subfractionated on these columns. Thus, the phospholipids of rats' liver have been separated into five fractions by elution with mixtures of chloroform and methanol in different proportions. Columns of alumina can also be used for fractionation of phospholipids. Fatty acids can be separated from one another on "reversed phase" columns with paraffin oil used as the stationary phase and mixtures of acetone and water used for elution.

D. Fractionation by paper chromatography

Chromatography on paper impregnated with silicic acid has been used for the fractionation of phospholipids.

E. Fractionation by thin-layer chromatography

In thin-layer chromatography a powdered adsorbent, such as silicic acid, is mixed with a binder, such as Plaster of Paris and water, and distributed as a thin layer on a glass plate. After drying, the plate is treated similarly to a sheet of filter paper in paper chromatography. The mixture to be fractionated is spotted or streaked near one edge of the plate, which is then dipped in a trough of solvent which moves up the plate by capillary attraction. The advantages over paper chromatography are that fractionation is complete in less than one hour, and the spots remain small so that fractionation is better. Also, although smaller quantities of material can be detected than with paper, much larger quantities can be put on the plate if desired.

Thin-layer chromatography is proving extremely useful for fractionating lipids. Silica gel is the most useful adsorbent and the fractionated lipids are detected in ultraviolet light or by spraying with sulphuric acid, aqueous iodine, antimony trichloride, or other reagents. The following are some examples of many separations that have been made. The methyl esters of natural fatty acids containing from ten to twenty-four carbons can be separated from one another on thin layers of silica gel impregnated with silicone oil. The developing solvent is a mixture of acetonitrile, acetic acid, and water. The spots are detected by exposing the plates to iodine vapour, after spraying with a solution of α-cyclodextrin, when they appear white on a purple background. Triglycerides can be fractionated on thin layers of tetradecane-standardised paraffin and kieselguhr, using a mixture of acetone and acetonitrile saturated with the paraffin for development. Phospholipids can be fractionated on thin layers of silica gel using a mixture of chloroform, methanol, and water for development.

F. Fractionation by gas-liquid chromatography

Gas-liquid chromatography is basically a varient of column chromatography. A glass tube at a controlled temperature is packed with an inert powder such as kieselguhr. For lipid chromatography this is impregnated with a material such as paraffin grease, silicone grease, or esters of polyethylene glycol, which is liquid at the temperature of chromatography but has a negligible vapour pressure. The mixture to be separated is put on one end of the column and an inert gas such as argon is slowly blown through from that end. As the mixture to be separated is swept through, its components are retarded to varying extents according to their affinity for the column, and they therefore emerge with different and characteristic volumes of gas. They are detected and determined by thermal conductivity or other physical measurements on the emerging gas. Gas chromatography is particularly useful for analysing mixtures of fatty acids after their conversion to methyl esters. The method is extremely sensitive. For example, free fatty acids, which occur in blood plasma at about 10 μg/100 ml, can be determined and many have been detected which were not known to be there.

G. Fractionation by counter-current distribution

This technique has already been described (p. 129). It has been found useful for fractionating some phospholipids. For example, the phospholipids of brain have been fractionated between the two phases of a mixture of petroleum ether and ethanol.

2. Simple Lipids: Fatty Acids, Fats, Wax Esters, and Sterol Esters

Simple lipids are fatty acids and their esters with alcohols. The alcohol is glycerol in fats, a monohydric aliphatic alcohol containing sixteen or more carbon atoms in wax esters, and cholesterol or another sterol in sterol esters.

A. Fats

Fats are mixtures of triglycerides—compounds in which each of the three hydroxyl groups of glycerol is esterified with a fatty acid. There is no sharp distinction between fats and oils, and technically *fat* is used to describe both. In common language "oil" refers to a liquid, but fats are of course liquid in live mammals. Triglycerides have the general formula:

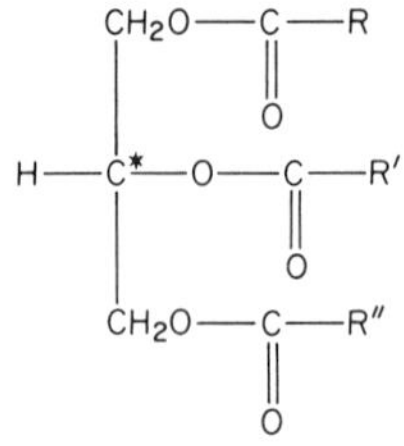

$$
\begin{array}{l}
\mathrm{CH_2O-\overset{\displaystyle O}{\overset{\displaystyle \|}{C}}-R} \\[2ex]
\mathrm{H-\overset{*}{C}-O-\overset{\displaystyle O}{\overset{\displaystyle \|}{C}}-R'} \\[2ex]
\mathrm{CH_2O-\overset{\displaystyle O}{\overset{\displaystyle \|}{C}}-R''}
\end{array}
$$

where RCOOH, R'COOH and R''COOH are fatty acids. When RCOOH and R''COOH differ the carbon marked with an asterisk is asymmetric.

It is probable that in fats only one enantiomer of each asymmetric triglyceride is present, but this is not certain and there is no evidence as to their configurations. In a "simple" triglyceride the three fatty acids are identical, while in a "mixed" triglyceride they are not:

$$CH_2OOC(CH_2)_{16}CH_3$$
$$H\text{---}\overset{|}{\underset{|}{C}}\text{---}OOC(CH_2)_{16}CH_3$$
$$CH_2OOC(CH_2)_{16}CH_3$$

Tristearin
(Simple)

$$CH_2OOC(CH_2)_{14}CH_3$$
$$H\text{---}\overset{|}{\underset{|}{C}}\text{---}OOC(CH_2)_{16}CH_3$$
$$CH_2OOC(CH_2)_{16}CH_3$$

α−Palmito−α′β distearin
(Mixed)

$$CH_2OOC(CH_2)_7CH\text{=}CH(CH_2)_7CH_3$$
$$H\text{---}\overset{|}{\underset{|}{C}}\text{---}OOC(CH_2)_{14}CH_3$$
$$CH_2OOC(CH_2)_{16}CH_3$$

Oleopalmitostearin
(Mixed)

On hydrolysis, fats give a mixture of glycerol and fatty acids. Because fats are insoluble in water, hydrolysis with dilute acid is not very effective. But in 0.5 N potassium hydroxide in 95% ethanol under reflux it is completed in a few hours. After removal of the ethanol under reduced pressure and acidification, the fatty acids can be extracted with ether or petroleum ether.

Until recently the analysis of a mixture of fatty acids was difficult, but modern methods of fractionation, of which gas-liquid chromatography is the most important, have simplified it. The fatty acids that are most abundant in fats (Table 5) have a straight hydrocarbon chain terminating

Table 5. *Principal fatty acids of triglycerides*

Butyric	$CH_3(CH_2)_2COOH$
Caproic	$CH_3(CH_2)_4COOH$
Caprylic	$CH_3(CH_2)_6COOH$
Capric	$CH_3(CH_2)_8COOH$
Lauric	$CH_3(CH_2)_{10}COOH$
Myristic	$CH_3(CH_2)_{12}COOH$
Palmitic	$CH_3(CH_2)_{14}COOH$
Stear	$CH_3(CH_2)_{16}COOH$
Oleic	$CH_3(CH_2)_7CH\text{=}CH(CH_2)_7COOH$
Palmitoleic	$CH_3(CH_2)_5CH\text{=}CH(CH_2)_7COOH$
Linoleic	$CH_3(CH_2)_4CH\text{=}CH\ CH_2CH\text{=}CH(CH_2)_7COOH$
Linolenic	$CH_3CH_2\ CH\text{=}CH\ CH_2CH\text{=}CHCH_2CH\text{=}CH(CH_2)_7COOH$

in a carboxyl group and have an even number of carbon atoms. The saturated fatty acids are members of the homologous series that begins with acetic and propionic acid. The unsaturated fatty acids have the same structure but with one or more double bonds inserted along the hydrocarbon chain. The hydrogen atoms on either side of these double bonds are, with rare exceptions, *cis* as in oleic acid:

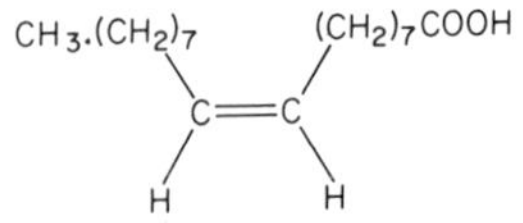

$$CH_3.(CH_2)_7 \quad (CH_2)_7COOH$$
$$\diagdown \qquad \diagup$$
$$C = C$$
$$\diagup \qquad \diagdown$$
$$H \qquad H$$

Fatty acids of similar structure but with odd numbers of carbon atoms are usually present in traces and occasionally in larger amounts. Branched chain acids, such as isovaleric acid, $(CH_3)_2CHCH_2COOH$, also occur in small amounts in many fats.

Table 6 shows the quantities of the main components in the fatty acid mixture that is released on the hydrolysis of certain fats. The composition varies from sample to sample and the values are only approximate. Plant fats, such as olive oil and linseed oil (Table 6) usually have a high proportion of unsaturated fatty acids, which accounts for their low melting points. In general, oleic acid is the most abundant unsaturated

Table 6. *Fatty acid composition of certain fats*
(Percent by weight of total acids)

Fatty acid	Olive oil	Linseed oil	Pig depot fat	Cow's milk fat
C_4 to C_{12} saturated	—	—	—	10
Myristic	—	—	—	10
Palmitic	15	7	30	26
Stearic	2	5	15	13
Oleic	70	25	45	32
Linoleic	12	20	5	—
Linolenic	—	40	—	—

fatty acid, but in some plant fats, such as hemp oil, linoleic and linolenic acids together comprise over 70% of the fatty acid mixture. Palmitic acid is the most abundant saturated fatty acid in plant fats, but fats of the *Lauraceae* contain high proportions of lauric acid, and those of the *Myristicaceae* high proportions of myristic acid.

Animal depot fats generally have a lower proportion of unsaturated fatty acids. Their composition is influenced by that of the food fat. In pigs, for example, a diet rich in corn oil, which has a high proportion of unsaturated fatty acids, gives an "oily" carcass fat, but a change to a diet rich in cottonseed oil a few weeks before slaughter gives a more desirable hard fat. Mammals cannot synthesise linoleic or linolenic acids, and ox and sheep fats are low in these acids since those in the diet are hydrogenated by the rumen microorganisms. Other unsaturated fatty acids, including palmitoleic acid are synthesised by mammalian tissues. Milk fat of ruminants has a higher proportion of saturated fatty acids from C_4 to C_{14} than depot fats, and milk fat of other mammals also has a higher proportion of C_{10} to C_{14} acids.

Methods have been devised for rapidly characterising the fatty acid mixture of a particular fat. One is to determine the "saponification value" which is the number of milligrammes of potassium hydroxide required to hydrolyse one gramme of fat. This gives an indication of the average molecular weight of the fatty acids, since less potassium hydroxide is required as the molecular weight increases. Unsaturation can be determined by the "iodine value": the number of grammes of iodine that combine with 100 gm of fat. The iodine combines at the double bonds of unsaturated fatty acids. Fatty acids containing twelve or less carbon atoms largely volatilise when steam is passed through a mixture of fatty acids. The proportion of steam-volatile fatty acids is indicated by the Reichert-Meissl value. These methods of characterising a fatty acid mixture are less important now that a complete analysis can be easily done by gas chromatography.

The physical properties of fatty acids are strongly influenced by the fact that they combine a nonpolar, hydrophobic hydrocarbon chain with the polar, hydrophilic carboxyl group. For example, if a small amount of a fatty acid is spread on an aqueous surface a single layer of molecules is formed. The carboxyl groups become hydrogen bonded to water molecules, and the hydrocarbon chains project perpendicularly from the surface. Again, in solution in solvents such as hexane, fatty acid molecules form dimers by hydrogen bonding between pairs of carboxyl groups:

In a saturated fatty acid free rotation can occur between every pair of carbon atoms in the hydrocarbon chain. Conformational analysis suggests that, in solution, almost every carbon of a saturated fatty acid is in a staggered conformation (see p. 12) relative to its neighbours; and that the front end of the hydrocarbon chain attached to any one carbon (R below) is *trans* to the rear end attached to the adjacent carbon (R' below):

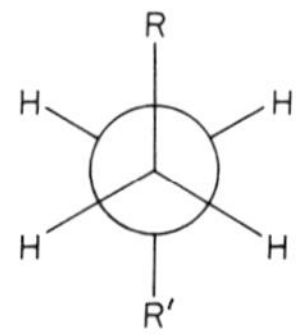

As a result, the carbon-carbon bonds are arranged in a zig-zag. Thus stearic acid may be represented:

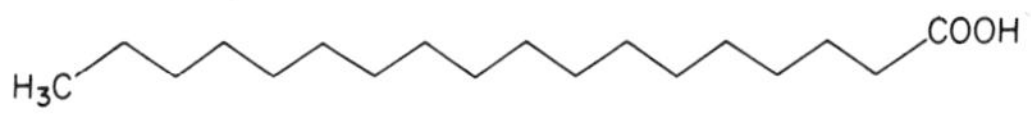

If the molecule contains one or more *cis* double bonds the zig-zag will be bent, as in oleic acid:

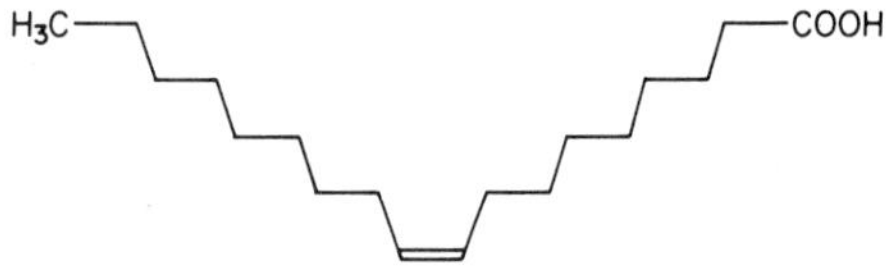

But if the double bonds are *trans* it remains straight:

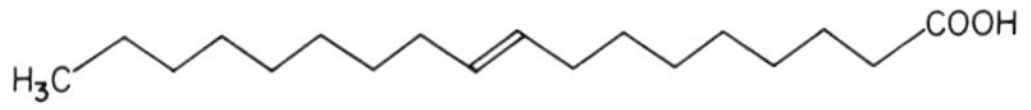

These conclusions are confirmed by X-ray diffraction measurements. The molecules in a crystal of a saturated fatty acid are all in the zig-zag conformation, and are bound into dimers by hydrogen bonding between carboxyl groups. These pairs of molecules are packed side by side to form layers whose width roughly equals the length of two molecules. These layers are the basis of the flaky structure of fatty acid crystals. Unsaturated fatty acids with *trans* double bonds will co-crystallise with saturated fatty acids, but those with *cis* bouble bonds will not do so because of their bent hydrocarbon chains.

Once the composition of the fatty acid mixture formed on the hydrolysis of a particular fat has been found the problem still remains of determining the number of kinds of triglyceride that are present in the original fat, and the structure of each. Triglycerides are difficult to separate and their structures are difficult to prove. As a result the complete triglyceride composition of a fat has never been determined. The number of triglycerides that could be formed from the mixture of fatty acids yielded by a fat is very large. From n fatty acids, $(n^3 + n^2)/2$ different triglycerides could be formed without counting enantiomers. Thus a mixture of six fatty acids could yield 126 different triglycerides.

Analyses show that fats are in fact complex mixtures of triglycerides, most of which are "mixed". However, the fatty acids are not distributed at random on the glycerol hydroxyls as they are when glycerol is chemically esterified with a mixture of fatty acids. Evidence for this is as follows. When a mixed triglyceride is heated with a catalyst the fatty acids migrate from one hydroxyl to another until a random mixture of all possible triglycerides is formed. If a fat is subjected to this treatment its properties change. Cottonseed oil, for example, is converted to a solid fat. Had the fatty acids in the fat originally been distributed at random no change in properties would have occurred. Again, the proportion of the glycerol molecules in a fat that are esterified with three saturated fatty acids can be determined. The fat is oxidised with permanganate when unsaturated fatty acids are severed at their double bonds, with the formation of carboxyl groups. Triglycerides which contain unsaturated fatty acids thus become acidic, and can be extracted with alkali from those that contain only saturated fatty acids. It is found that the proportion of glycerol molecules with three saturated fatty acids is lower than would occur in a random arrangement. Thus 63% of the fatty acid molecules yielded by borneo tallow are saturated. If these were distributed at random on the glycerol hydroxyls, 25% of the glycerol molecules would be attached to three saturated fatty acids. In fact only 5% are. Analysis of the triglycerides of milk fat has also shown that the fatty acids are not randomly arranged. A number of rules have been suggested to describe the arrangement of the fatty acids in fats but none is completely satisfactory.

B. Waxes

Waxes are a group of compounds extracted from living tissues by lipid solvents. They include wax esters—esters of long chain fatty acids with monohydric aliphatic alcohols containing sixteen or more carbons such as cetyl alcohol, $CH_3(CH_2)_{14}CH_2OH$. Since the polar ester groups are a very small portion of these molecules they have similar properties to the higher paraffins which are also found in waxes.

C. Sterol esters

The only sterol esters that appear to be important in mammals are cholesterol esters:

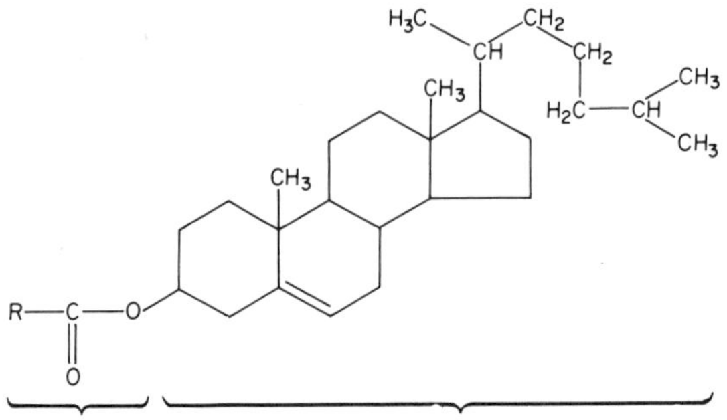

They occur in blood plasma, liver, and the adrenals. They can be hydrolysed by heating under reflux with alcoholic potassium hydroxide when they yield cholesterol (see p. 176) and a fatty acid. After diluting the hydrolysate with water, cholesterol can be extracted with ether. Then, after acidification, the fatty acids can also be extracted with ether. The fatty acids are the same as those that occur in triglycerides, although the relative proportions of the different kinds are different. Cholesterol esters of plasma, for example, have a high proportion of linoleic acid.

Esters of sterols other than cholesterol occur in some organisms.

3. Complex Lipids

The group of compounds known as "complex lipids" have a wide range of structures, but they each contain a hydrophilic group, such as a phosphoric acid residue, together with a hydrophobic group, such as a fatty acid side chain. They principally occur associated with proteins in cell membranes, including those of nuclei, mitochondria, and the endoplasmic reticulum. They are difficult to classify in a simple way, but the two main groups are outlined below. Complex lipids that contain phosphorus are also known as phospholipids.

A. Derivatives of diglycerides (glycerolipids)

These complex lipids are derivatives of diglycerides of the structure:

170

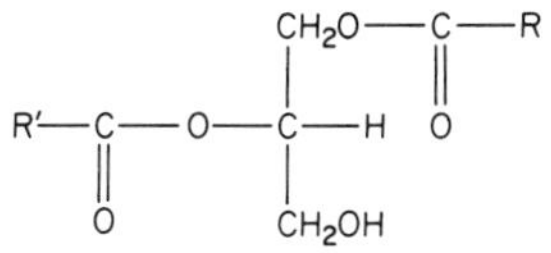

$$CH_2O-C-R$$
$$R'-C-O-C-H \quad O$$
$$O \qquad CH_2OH$$

where R and R' are fatty acid residues mostly with 14 to 22 carbon atoms, with 16 and 18 predominating. C_2 of the glycerol residue is asymmetric and the correct Fischer projection is shown here. In the glycerolipids the glycerol hydroxyl is combined, by the elimination of water, with a range of molecules the most important of which are orthophosphoric acid, choline phosphate, ethanolamine phosphate, serine phosphate, glycerol phosphate, myo-inositol phosphate, and galactose or certain other carbohydrates: (see next page).

B. Derivatives of N-acylsphingosines (sphingolipids)

Sphingosine has the structure:

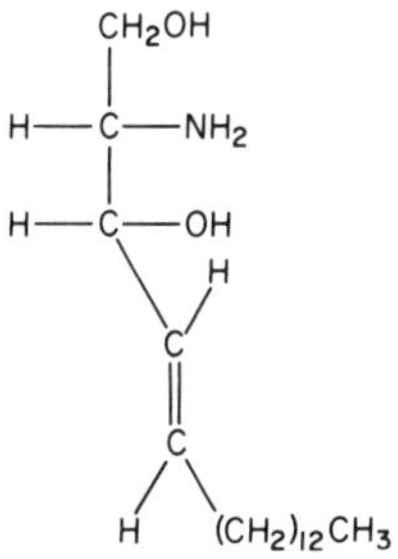

$$CH_2OH$$
$$H-C-NH_2$$
$$H-C-OH$$
$$H$$
$$C$$
$$C$$
$$H \qquad (CH_2)_{12}CH_3$$

It is seen that configurations on the asymmetric carbons C_2 and C_3 are both D-, and that the arrangement of the hydrogens across the double bond is *trans*.

N-acylsphingosines have the structure:

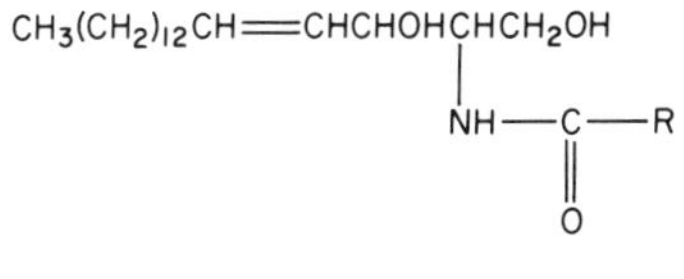

$$CH_3(CH_2)_{12}CH=CHCHOHCHCH_2OH$$
$$NH-C-R$$
$$O$$

where R is a saturated or unsaturated fatty acid residue which usually has twenty-four carbons. An example is lignoceric acid $CH_3(CH_2)_{22}COOH$.

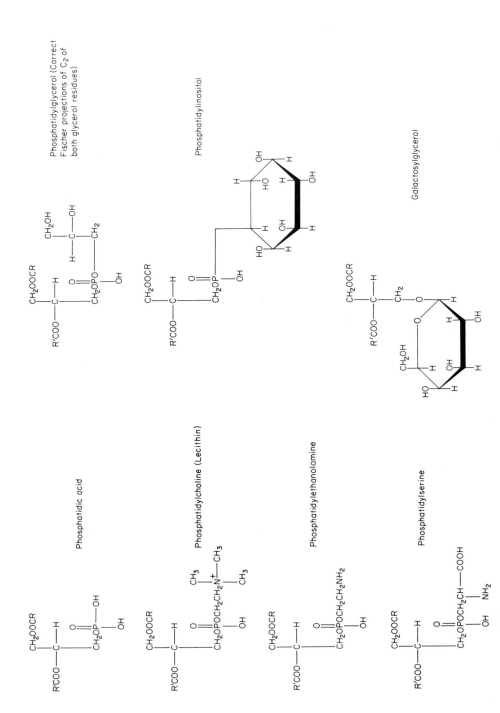

Phosphatidic acid

Phosphatidylcholine (Lecithin)

Phosphatidylethanolamine

Phosphatidylserine

Phosphatidylglycerol (Correct Fischer projections of C_2 of both glycerol residues)

Phosphatidylinositol

Galactosylglycerol

172

When N-acylsphingosines are drawn as follows it becomes apparent that their structures are very similar to those of α,β-diglycerides:

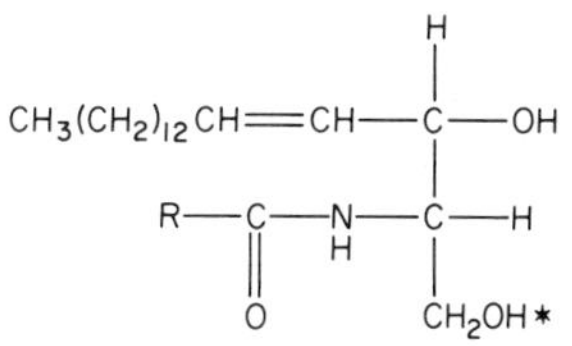

Sphingolipids are formed by reaction of other molecules with the hydroxyl marked with an asterisk, and their structures are therefore very similar to those of the complex lipids derived from diglycerides. The principal molecules which can be combined at this hydroxyl by the elimination of water are choline phosphate and a carbohydrate such as galactose:

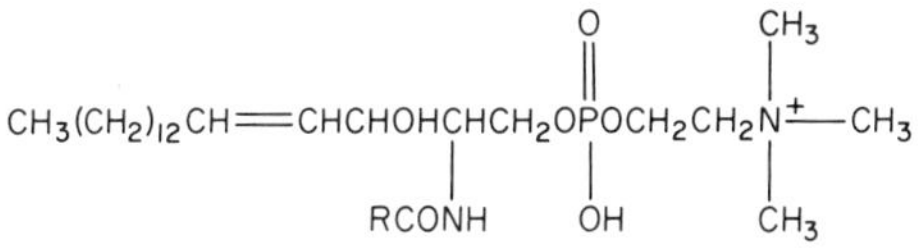

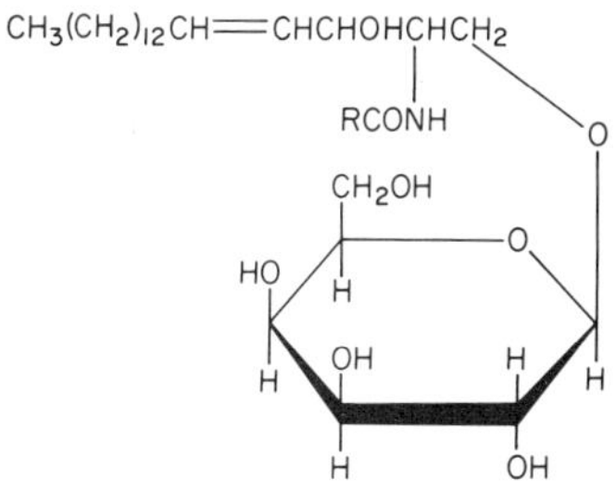

There are other similar complex lipids in which sphingosine is replaced by a closely related compound such as phytosphingosine. All these lipids are classified as sphingolipids.

4. Isoprenoids

Isoprenoids are compounds, found mostly in plants but also in animals, which can be considered to be built up from units of isoprene (β-methylbutadiene):

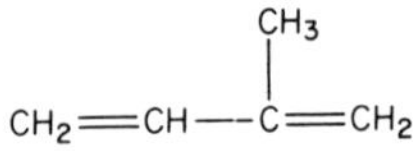

$$CH_2\!=\!CH\!-\!\!\underset{\displaystyle |}{\overset{\displaystyle CH_3}{C}}\!=\!CH_2$$

Since isoprene has five carbons, isoprenoid hydrocarbons mostly have multiples of five carbons. The volatile (or "essential") oils of plants are isoprenoids and their occurrence in turpentine oil has led to them being known chemically as "terpenes". All these compounds are synthesised in plants from acetate via the pyrophosphate of isopentenol:

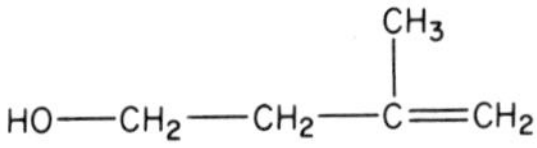

$$HO\!-\!CH_2\!-\!CH_2\!-\!\underset{\displaystyle |}{\overset{\displaystyle CH_3}{C}}\!=\!CH_2$$

A simple terpene is limonene. The dextrorotatory form occurs in plants, but the racemic mixture can be synthesised merely by heating isoprene:

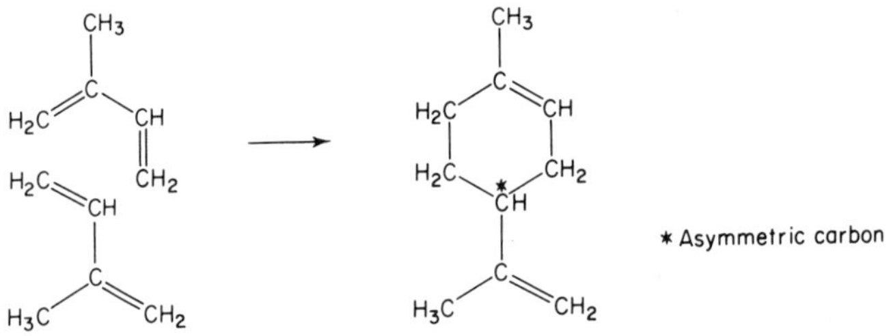

* Asymmetric carbon

Some other terpene hydrocarbons are:

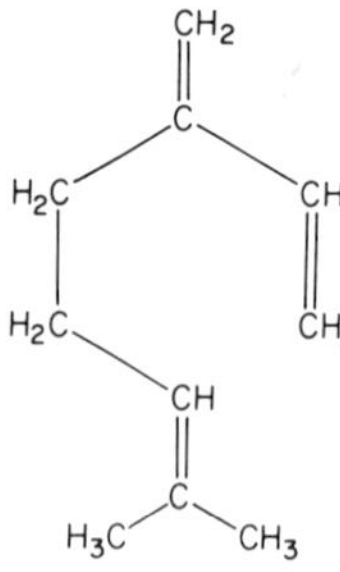

Myrcene 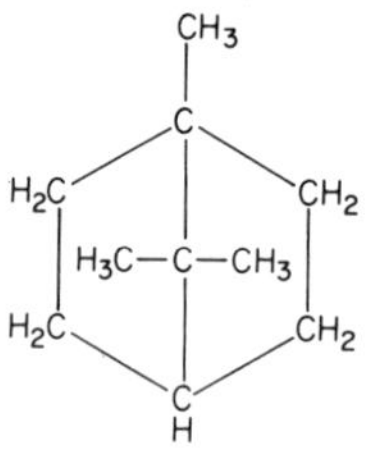   Camphane 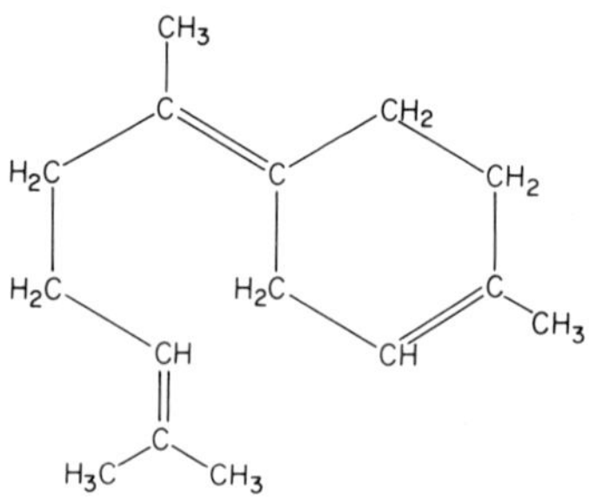   Bisabolene

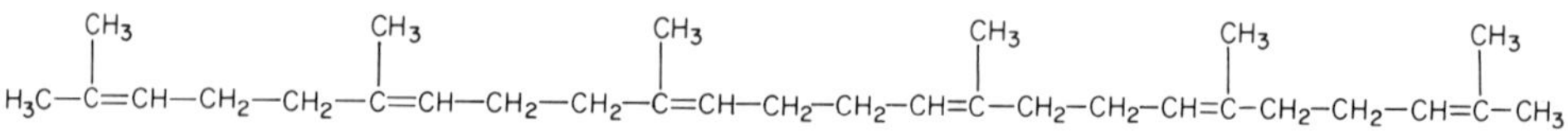

Squalene

Squalene is an intermediate in the biosynthesis of steroids. Examples of terpene derivatives are geraniol, a constituent of oil of roses:

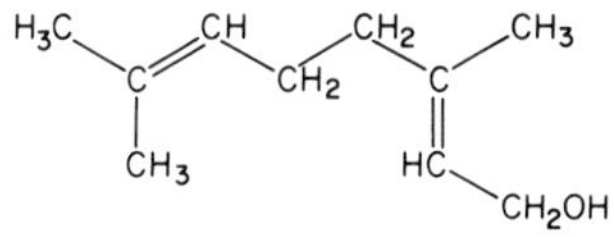

and camphor (shown in a projection formula):

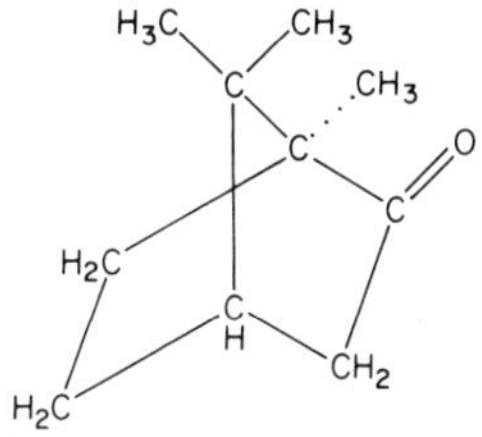

Other important isoprenoids are the carotenoids which largely occur associated with plant and animal fats. Their structures are all related to that of α-carotene ($C_{40}H_{56}$):

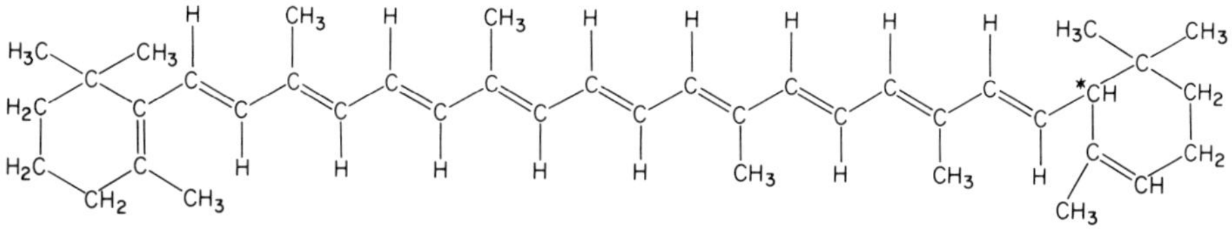

*Asymmetric carbon. Note *trans* arrangement at each double bond

An important carotenoid is vitamin A ($C_{20}H_{30}O$):

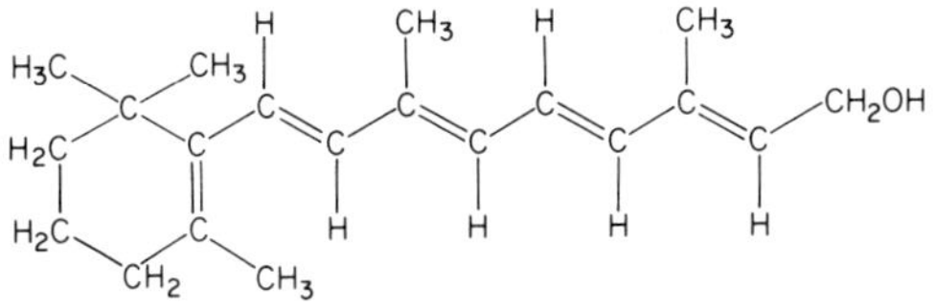

Rubber is an isoprene polymer. Gutta-percha, a component of rubber, has the structure:

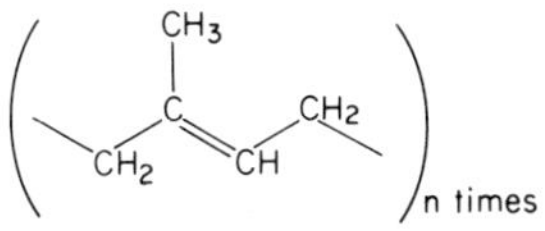

5. Steroids

Steroids are a group of compounds with a common basic ring structure in which a reduced phenanthrene ring is fused to a five-membered ring as in the hydrocarbon:

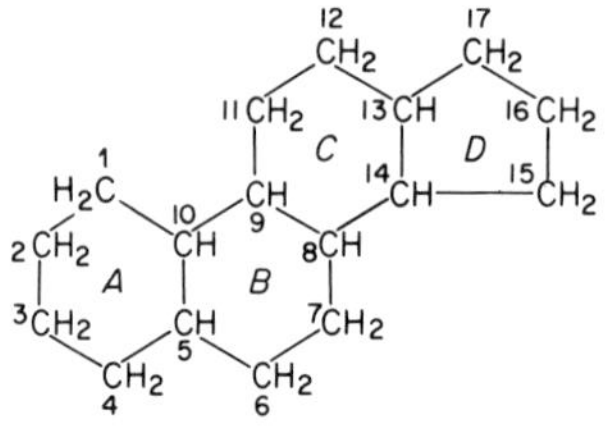

or

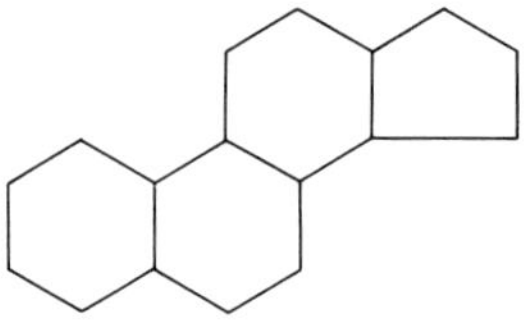

The four rings are lettered A, B, C, and D and the carbon atoms are numbered as shown. All steroids have a side chain attached to carbon 17. Many also have an alcoholic hydroxyl attached to the ring system, and are known as "sterols". The most common sterol is cholesterol which occurs in most animal tissues:

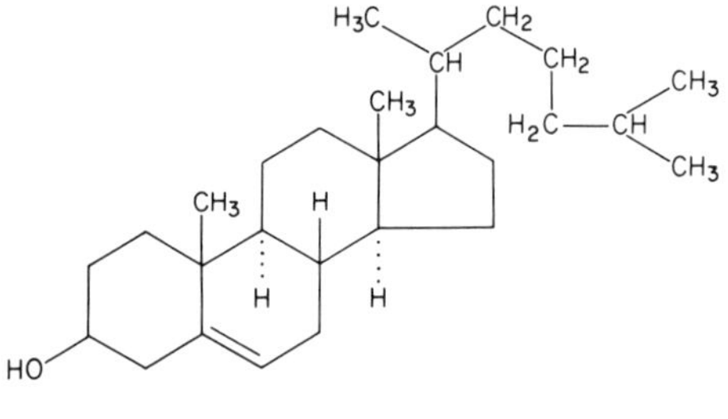

In the parent hydrocarbon shown above, each pair of hydrogens at the ring junctions (C_5 and C_{10}, C_8 and C_9, and C_{13} and C_{14}) can be *cis* or *trans* as in the decalins (see p. 20). Moreover, each of these carbons is asymmetric (linked to four different groups) and hence two *cis* and two *trans* isomers are possible at each ring junction. Those at the junction of rings A and B may, for example, be represented:

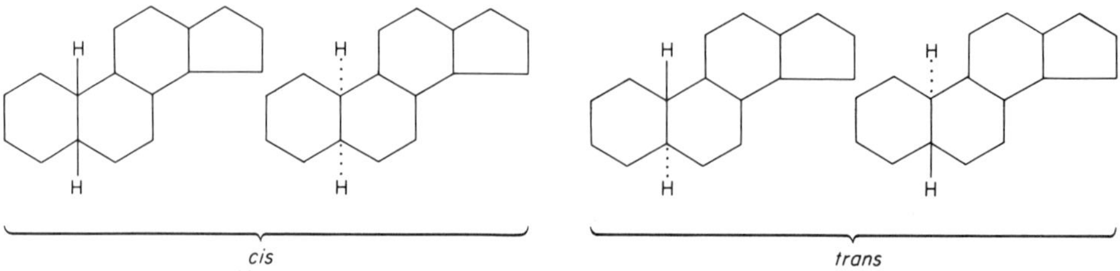

cis

trans

The ring system is understood to be in the plane of the paper and dotted bonds attached to the ring are directed below the plane of the paper (known as α-orientated), and solid bonds are directed above it, (β-orientated). Since there are six asymmetric carbons there are $2^6 = 64$ different steroisomers of this hydrocarbon. In steroids the side chain attached to C_{17} makes this carbon asymmetric so increasing the number of stereoisomers to 128. There are usually additional asymmetric carbons. Thus in cholesterol C_3 and C_{20} are asymmetric although C_5 is not. Hence cholesterol is one of 256 stereoisomers: One of these is its enantiomer, which has the mirror-image configuration on every asymmetric carbon, while the remaining 254 are diastereoisomers with the mirror-image configuration on only some of the carbons (see p. 48).

In natural steroids the angular methyl groups attached to C_{10} and C_{13}, and the side chain attached to C_{17} are all β-orientated. All natural sterols have a hydroxyl at C_3 which is β as in cholesterol. Such sterols react with the glycoside digitonin in alcoholic solution to form an insoluble precipitate. This reaction is the basis for the microdetermination of cholesterol in body fluids. As shown in the above formula of cholesterol, the hydrogens at C_8 and C_9 are respectively β and α orientated while that at C_{14} is α. Hence the junctions of rings B and C, and of rings C and D, are *trans* as they are in almost all natural steroids.

Two sterols formed by the hydrogenation of the double bond between C_5 and C_6 of cholesterol are found in animals. They are cholestanol in which the hydrogen at C_5 is α and coprostanol in which it is β:

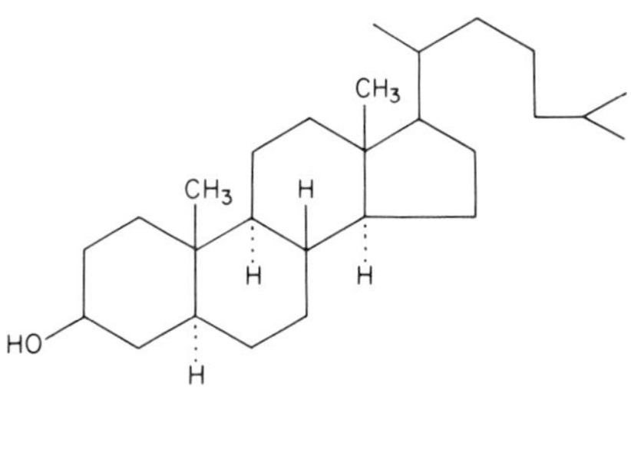

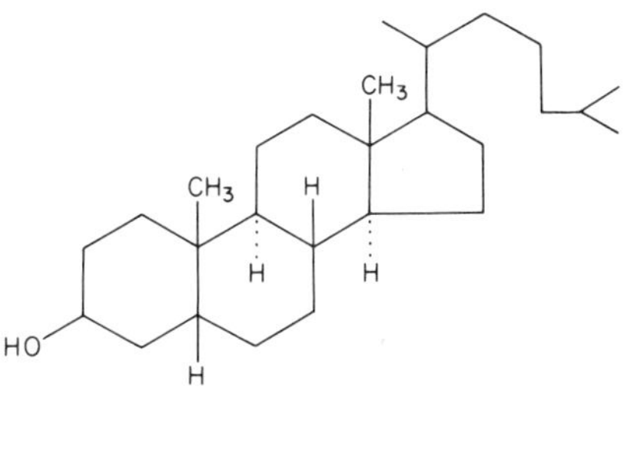

In cholestanol the A and B rings are therefore *trans* while in coprostanol they are *cis*.

The principal plant sterols differ from cholesterol mainly in the side chain attached to C_{17}. Stigmasterol for example differs from cholesterol only in the side chain and has the structure:

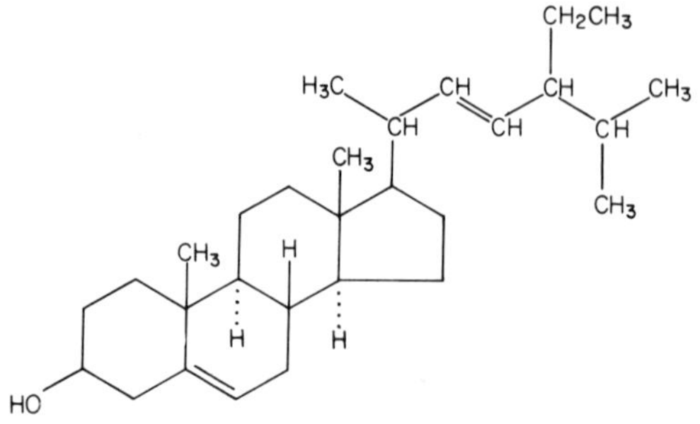

Ergosterol has one less methyl group in the side chain and a double bond between C_7 and C_8.

Many hormones are steroids. Thus estradiol has the structure:

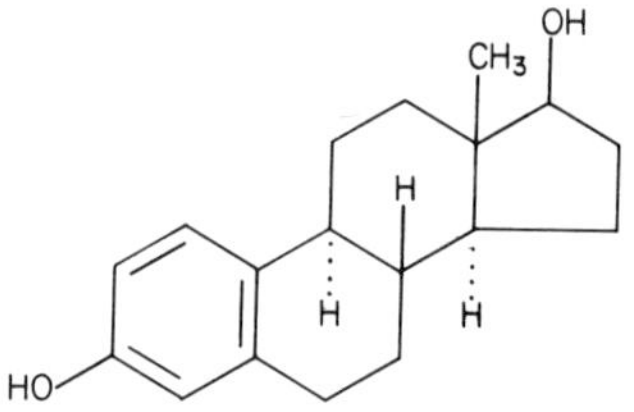

In the above steroid formulae the ring system is represented as flat, which in fact it is not. As already mentioned, in all natural steroids, the junctions of rings B and C, and C and D, are *trans*. There is however one group of steroids, similar to cholestanol, in which rings A and B are *trans*, and another series, similar to coprostanol, in which they are *cis*. The conformations of cholestanol and coprostanol may be represented: (see next page).

As in *cis* and *trans*-decalin (see p. 20) the six-membered rings A, B, and C are all in the chair conformation. In cholestanol the hydroxyl on C_3 is equatorial while in coprostanol it is axial.

The recent understanding of the conformation of steroids has brought an increased understanding of their properties. Thus, an equatorial hydroxyl, being less sterically hindered than an axial one, is more easily esterified. It is also found that a secondary hydroxyl is more readily oxidised if the hydroxyl is axial and the hydrogen equatorial; also that sterols with equatorial hydroxyls tend to be more strongly absorbed on filter paper or alumina, and therefore tend to move more slowly on chromatography, than sterols with axial hydroxyls.

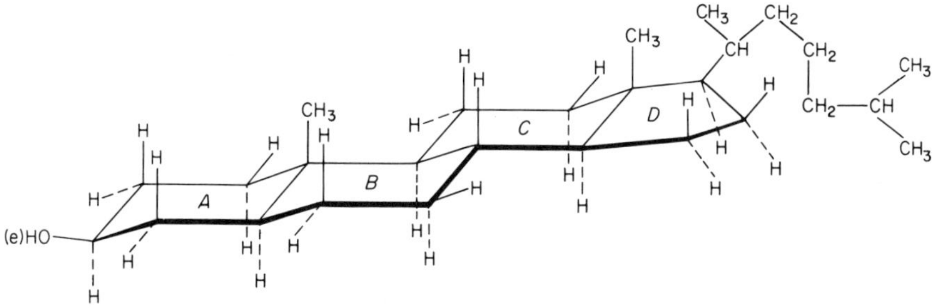

Cholestanol

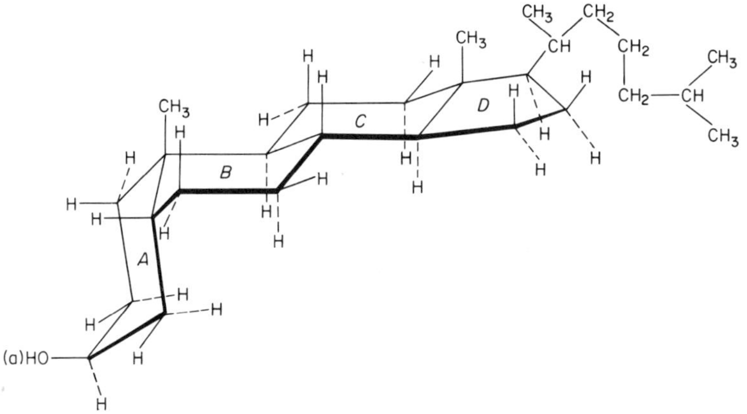

Coprostanol

6. Porphyrins and Chlorins

Porphyrins are derivatives of porphin:

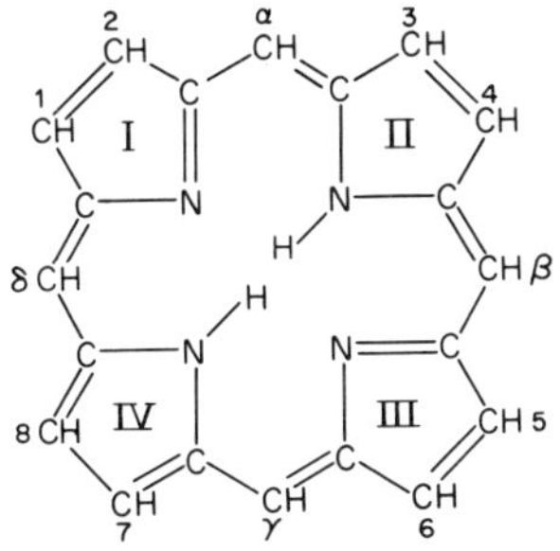

The pyrrole rings are numbered I to IV, their β-carbons 1 to 8, and the four methene bridges α to δ as shown. It at one time appeared that two isomers of porphin and each of its derivatives might exist in which opposite, or adjacent, nitrogens bore hydrogens:

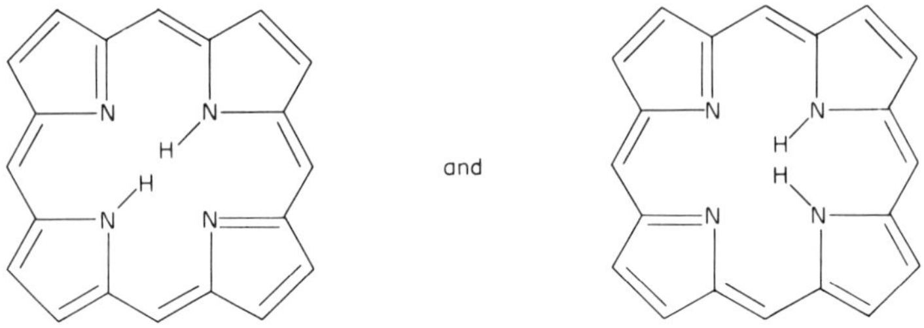

and

It now appears from spectroscopic studies that all four nitrogens are similarly involved in the bonding of the hydrogens, and hence distinct isomers of this type could not exist. Porphyrins play an important role in living organisms when complexed with iron and bound to proteins in hemoglobin, myoglobin, and the cytochromes. Chlorophylls, which are responsible for the absorption of light energy by green plants, are complexes of magnesium with derivatives of dihydroporphin (chlorin):

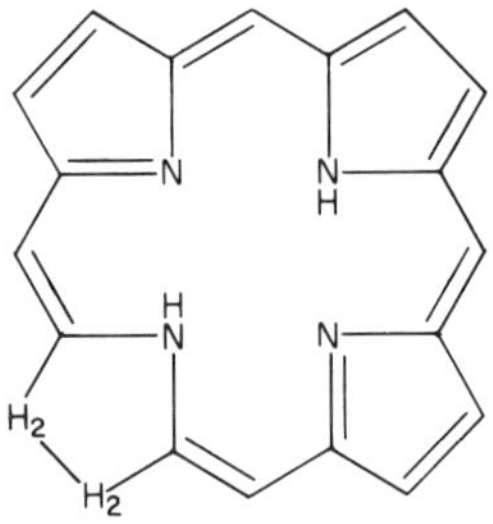

Other metalloporphyrins also occur in living organisms.

In natural porphyrins the β-carbons of each of the four pyrrole rings carry substituents other than hydrogen. Frequent substituents are -CH_3, -$CH=CH_2$ and -$CH_2 \cdot CH_2 \cdot COOH$. Thus, protoporphyrin IX, which is combined with iron in hemoglobin, has the structure:

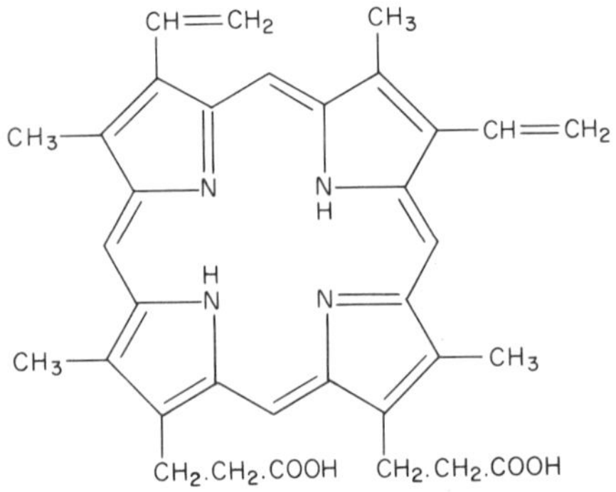

Every natural porphyrin has some substituents with acidic carboxyl groups, and hence the natural porphyrins are all amphoteric since their nitrogens are basic. Solutions of porphyrins absorb visible light. Their absorption spectra have four maxima, and the sizes of these, and the wave lengths at which they occur, can be correlated with the substituents on the β-carbons. Hence absorption spectra can aid in proving the structures of porphyrins.

The derivative of dihydroporphin that is combined with magnesium in chlorophyll a, one of the two main components of chlorophyll, is phaeophytin a:

Phytol

It is seen that this compound has a five-carbon ring between the pyrrole rings III and IV. Attached to β-carbon 7 is a propionic acid residue esterified with the isoprenoid alcohol phytol. The hydrogens attached to β-carbons 7 and 8 are *trans*. These carbons are also asymmetric. Phaeophytin a has a particular one of the two possible configurations on each of these carbons and is optically active. Phaeophytin b, which combines with magnesium to give chlorophyll b, has the same structure except for a -CHO group in place of -CH$_3$ on β-carbon 3. Unlike the natural porphyrins, neither of these chlorins has acidic side chains.

Porphyrins and chlorins will form complexes with divalent metals by replacement of the two hydrogens attached to nitrogens. The structure of any one of these complexes may be represented in a number of conventional formulae which differ only in the distribution of double and single bonds.

Index

185